AS Fast-Track

Physics

Basil Donnelly

Jeremy Spackman

Series consultants **Geoff Black** and **Stuart Wall**

Page designer **Michelle Cannatella**

Cover designer **Kube Ltd**

Pearson Education Limited
Edinburgh Gate
Harlow
Essex CM20 2JE, England
and Associated Companies throughout the world

ISBN 0 582 43238–3

British Library Cataloguing-in-Publication Data

A catalogue record for this book is available from the British Library.

Set by 3 in Optima and Tekton
Printed by Ashford Colour Press, Gosport, Hants, UK

Contents

TWO WAYS TO USE THIS BOOK...

This book is designed to be used:

Either

- On its own – work through all the exercises for a quick run-through of your subject. This will take you about 24 hours altogether.

or

- As part of the *Revision Express* system:

1 Read through the topic in the *Revision Express A-level Study Guide* (or similar book).

2 Work through the exercises in this book.

3 Go to www.revision-express.com for extra exam questions and model answers.

4 For even more depth and detail, refer back to your textbook or class notes, and visit the web links from www.revision-express.com.

HOW THE BOOK WORKS

The book is divided into two-page revision sessions. To make your revision really effective, study one session at a time.

Have a short break between sessions – that way you'll learn more!

Each session has two parts:

1st page: the first page on each topic contains interactive exercises to nail down the basics. Follow the instructions in the margin and write your answers in the spaces provided.

2nd page: the second page contains exam questions. Sometimes you'll answer the exam question directly, but more often you'll use it as a starting point for in-depth revision exercises. In each case, follow the extra instructions in the margin.

REMEMBER: the answers in the back are for the revision exercises – they are not necessarily model answers to the exam questions themselves. For model answers to a selection of exam questions go to www.revision-express.com.

All the pages are hole-punched, so you can remove them and put them in your folder.

TRACK YOUR PROGRESS

The circles beside each topic heading let you track your progress.

If a topic is hard, fill in one circle. If it's easy, fill in all three. If you've only filled in one or two circles go back to the topic later.

TOPIC HEADING

EXAM BOARDS

You might not need to work through every session in this book. Check that your exam board is listed above the topic heading before you start a session.

(AS) AQA EDEXCEL OCR WJEC

This book covers the most popular topics. For full information about your syllabus, contact the relevant exam board or go to their website.

AQA
(Assessment and Qualifications Alliance)
Publications department, Stag Hill House,
Guildford, Surrey GU2 5XJ – www.aqa.org.uk

EDEXCEL
Stuart House, 32 Russell Square, London
WC1B 5DN – www.edexcel.org.uk

OCR
(Oxford, Cambridge and Royal Society of Arts)
1 Hills Road, Cambridge CB2 1GG –
www.ocr.org.uk

DON'T FORGET

Exam questions have been specially written for this book. Ask your teacher or the exam board for the official sample papers to add to the questions given here.

COMMENTS PLEASE!

However you use this book, we'd welcome your comments. Just go to www.revision-express.com and tell us what you think!

GOOD LUCK!

Scalars and vectors

If direction matters, you are dealing with a *vector* quantity. New rules of addition and subtraction apply. Can you apply them?

VECTOR QUANTITIES ○○○

List as many vector quantities as you can in the space provided.

VECTOR ADDITION AND SUBTRACTION ○○○

Vectors can be added using scale drawings. If two forces F_1 and F_2 act at an angle θ, their resultant can be found by the **parallelogram rule**.

Draw a diagram to illustrate the parallelogram rule.

Now sketch the parallelogram you would use to subtract F_2 from F_1.

Vector subtraction

State the rule for subtracting one vector from another.

RESOLVING VECTORS INTO PERPENDICULAR COMPONENTS ○○○

Any vector can be resolved into perpendicular component vectors. This allows us to consider horizontal and vertical motion separately, or to distinguish between forces acting along a plane and normal (at 90°) to a plane.

Show how you would resolve an arrow's velocity v into a horizontal component v_x and a vertical component v_y.

Why do we usually resolve velocity into horizontal and vertical components?

Turn the page for some exam questions on this topic ➤

EXAM QUESTION 1

●●●

Two forces act simultaneously on a body. The size of the resultant force is 160 N. One of the forces is 100 N in magnitude.

Put a tick next to each force which could give a resultant of 160 N when added to a 100 N force.

(a) Which of the following forces could be the second force?

50 N ☐   250 N ☐   150 N ☐   300 N ☐

(b) If the size of the second force is 120 N, use a scale drawing or another method to find the angle between the two forces.

Use a scale drawing to find the angle. You will need to use a pair of compasses. Use the space opposite to show how you did it.

EXAM QUESTION 2

●●●

An aeroplane flies horizontally at a steady velocity of 100 m s^{-1}. It drops a small, heavy parcel. Assuming air resistance is negligible, find the parcel's speed 5.0 s later. Take $g = 9.81$ m s^{-2}.

Draw a sketch to help you.

EXAM QUESTION 3

●●●

A block rests on a rough board which is tilted at a gradient of 35°.

(a) Draw a free-body force diagram for the block.

LINKS
To find out more about free-body force diagrams, see pp. 17–18.

(b) If the block weighs 40 N, calculate the size of the frictional force preventing the block from sliding down the board.

(c) The board is thin and fragile. If the normal force acting on its surface exceeds 35 N, it will break. The board is slowly lowered towards the horizontal.

(i) Will it break?

(ii) If so, at what angle?

Forces and moments in equilibrium

This section is essentially about static objects. For any object to remain at rest, the forces and moments acting on and about each and every point must be balanced.

DON'T FORGET

You can add vectors together by drawing a sequence of arrows, tail to nose. If a body is in equilibrium, the nose of the last force arrow will touch the tail of the first, making a closed polygon.

> To check that the forces on the pulley are balanced, rearrange the force arrows to form a triangle.

FORCE POLYGONS   ○○○

Free-body force diagrams show all the forces acting on a body. If the body is static, the sum of the forces must equal zero, so the force vectors will add up (tail to nose) to form a closed polygon.

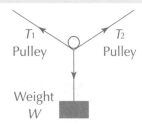

MOMENTS   ○○○

The moment of a force about a point is given by

> Write an equation and define terms.

In the diagram below, the moment about point P is 30 N m. Find the size of the force F.

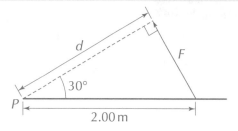

THE PRINCIPLE OF MOMENTS   ○○○

If a body is in rotational equilibrium,

> Complete the sentence to state the principle of moments in your own words.

STATICS PROBLEMS: TWO COMMON TYPES   ○○○

- Problems involving three (or occasionally more) forces, acting at different angles on the same body (effectively on the same point). To solve these problems, you can use

> Complete the sentence.

- Problems involving beams and rigid bodies, with forces acting at different points. To solve these, you need to use

> Complete the sentence.

Turn the page for some exam questions on this topic ➤

EXAM QUESTION 1 ●●●

An archer draws a bow by pulling on the bowstring with a horizontal force of 200 N, keeping the bowstring's tension above the arrow equal to the bowstring's tension below the arrow. Given the angles shown in the diagram, find this tension by scale drawing.

Draw a triangle of forces and find T, the tension in the bow.

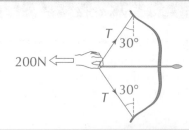

EXAM QUESTION 2 ●●●

EXAMINER'S SECRETS
Although the triangle of forces can be used to solve problems like this, it is often easier to resolve forces into horizontal and vertical components, then use the fact that the forces balance in each direction.

A cable-car is suspended on a cable between pylons A and B.

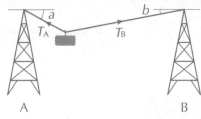

(a) If T_A is the tension in the cable on the side towards A and T_B is the tension on the side towards B, describe qualitatively the changes in T_A and T_B as the car makes its way from A to B. Explain your answer.

Considering only the horizontal components of the tension forces, find an equation linking T_A and T_B then use it to answer the question.

(b) If the cable-car weighs 5000 N and the distance between A and B is 200 m and the cable is 220 m long, calculate the maximum tension the cable must be capable of holding (assume the cable does not stretch and is very light).

EXAM QUESTION 3 ●●●

A painter stands on a rigid board supported by two trestles. The painter weighs 500 N and the board weighs 100 N. Given the dimensions shown, calculate the weight held by each trestle.

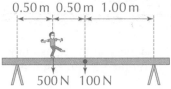

Write down the sequence of steps you followed to get the answer.

Ways of describing motion

The most concise way to describe motion is to use a graph.

DEFINITIONS ○○○

Define each term. Give its symbol and its SI unit.

Quantity	Symbol	Definition	SI unit
Displacement			
Velocity			
Acceleration			

DISTANCE–TIME GRAPHS AND DISPLACEMENT–TIME GRAPHS ○○○

Fill in the gaps.

In any journey, the distance travelled can only increase, so the gradient of a distance–time graph is always .... Instantaneous speed is equal to the .... of a distance–time graph.

Match the letter to the statement.

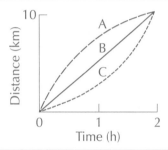

shows acceleration

shows constant speed

shows deceleration

Write the formula for average speed, then work out the answers.

What is the average speed of each object over the 10 km journey?

When the direction of travel matters, it makes more sense to use a displacement–time graph. Its gradient tells us an object's .... Sketch a displacement–time graph for a bouncing ball.

Start at maximum height (so the ball has a reason to fall).

VELOCITY–TIME GRAPHS ○○○

You can use a velocity–time graph to find a body's displacement and its acceleration at any instant (as well as its velocity).

Describe how you would determine each quantity from a velocity–time graph.

Displacement

Acceleration

Turn the page for some exam questions on this topic ➤

EXAM QUESTION 1

● ● ●

A beanbag is thrown up vertically in the air. When it lands, it does not bounce. Assume air resistance is negligible.

(a) Sketch a graph of its height above the ground against time.

(b) Sketch a graph of its velocity against time, taking upwards as the positive direction.

(c) Explain how you would determine the magnitude of the gravitational acceleration *g* from the velocity–time graph.

(d) If the effects of air resistance *were* significant, the velocity–time graph would change. Which region of the graph would then give the best estimate of *g*? Explain your answer.

EXAM QUESTION 2

● ● ●

The graph shows how a skydiver's downward velocity varied with time during a particular fall.

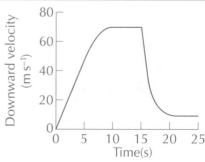

(a) When did the skydiver's parachute open?

(b) Describe and explain the motion shown in every 5 s interval.

(c) From what height did the skydiver fall? Show how you found it.

Equations of motion

The equations of motion are essential for solving problems involving constant acceleration.

SYMBOLS AND THEIR DEFINITIONS ○○○

Name and define each term. Give its SI unit and give a tick to each vector quantity.

Symbol	Definition	Unit	Tick if vector
s			
u			
v			
a			
t			

EXAMINER'S SECRETS
Your first step in solving any problem involving equations of motion should be to write down these five quantities and any values you're given. This helps to crystallize the problem in your mind.

EQUATIONS OF MOTION ○○○

Complete the three standard equations of motion:

$$v = \qquad\qquad\qquad\qquad (1)$$

$$s = \qquad\qquad\qquad\qquad (2)$$

$$v^2 = \qquad\qquad\qquad\qquad (3)$$

Show how the equation for velocity derives from the definition of acceleration.

Write an equation for displacement in terms of average velocity and time, then in terms of symbols u, v and t.

Replace v by $(u + at)$ and hence derive equation (2).

EXAMINER'S SECRETS
Manipulating equations gets easier the more often you do it. Be careful and don't rush. Get into good habits from the start. Give a separate line to every operation you perform on an equation.

CHANGING THE SUBJECT ○○○

What rules must be followed when you want to make a different term the subject of an equation?

Turn the page for some exam questions on this topic ➤

EXAM QUESTION 1

In a relay race, runner A has to pass the baton to runner B, who waits at the start of a 5.00 m changeover box. B can start running at any time, but A must successfully pass B the baton at some point within the box. A approaches B at a steady speed of 9.00 m s^{-1}.

> To answer this question, first write down what limits B's top speed within the box.

(a) If B can accelerate from rest at 5.50 m s^{-2}, when (i.e. how many seconds before the handover) should B set off?

IF YOU HAVE TIME
Try assuming B can accelerate faster, e.g. at 6.50 m s^{-2}, at least for a short time. Can you still work out when B should set off?

(b) Use your answer to calculate how far away A is from B when B starts running.

EXAM QUESTION 2

A bungee jumper falls freely from rest for 15.0 m before the bungee begins to stretch.

(a) Calculate their speed when the bungee just starts to stretch.

IF YOU HAVE TIME
Sketch a free-body force diagram for the bungee jumper (a) in free fall (b) when they have reached their top speed and (c) when the bungee is at maximum extension. Say which force is biggest in each case.

(b) Is this the jumper's top speed? Justify your answer.

(c) If the bungee brings the jumper to a halt in a further 5 m, calculate the jumper's average acceleration in this last 5 m.

EXAM QUESTION 3

A diver jumps from a springboard at a speed of 6.5 m s^{-1} and at an angle of 60° above the horizontal. The springboard is 0.60 m above the surface of the water.

(a) Calculate the maximum height reached above the water's surface.

(b) Calculate the diver's speed as they hit the water.

Projectiles

Projectiles are subject to gravity. Projectile problems require you to consider vertical and horizontal motion separately.

GRAVITATIONAL ACCELERATION   ○○○

Projectile problems set at AS level will normally include the assumption that air resistance is negligible. This allows us to treat vertical acceleration as constant (g) and to assume horizontal speed does not change.

Two balls roll off a table at different speeds. How would you calculate the horizontal distance each ball travels before hitting the ground?

> Assume you have all the information you need to solve the problem, i.e. the table's height and the initial speed of each ball.

RESOLVING HORIZONTAL AND VERTICAL MOTION   ○○○

> **SPEED LEARNING**
> Definitions of sine, cosine and tangent are summarized by **SohCahToa**.
> **S**ine: **o**pposite over **h**ypotenuse.
> **C**osine: **a**djacent over **h**ypotenuse.
> **T**angent: **o**pposite over **a**djacent.

A projectile has a velocity **v**, magnitude v, directed at an angle θ above the horizontal; write the magnitudes of the horizontal and vertical components (v_x and v_y) in terms of v and θ.

MAXIMUM HEIGHT, FLIGHT TIME AND RANGE   ○○○

> State which quantities are needed for each calculation.

(a) What information do you need for calculating maximum height?

(b) What information do you need for calculating flight time?

What information do you need for calculating range?

Calculate the maximum height and range of a golf ball hit at a speed of $45.0 \, \text{m s}^{-1}$ at $40.0°$ above the horizontal. Assume no air resistance.

> Take one step at a time. Write down the quantities you know. Calculate the maximum height reached. Work out the time for the flight. Work out the ball's range.

Turn the page for some exam questions on this topic ➤

For more on this topic, see pages 12–13 of the *Revision Express A-level Study Guide*

EXAM QUESTION 1

Balls A and B are thrown off a cliff at the same speed. A is thrown at angle θ above the horizontal, B at angle θ below the horizontal. Which hits the ground with the greatest speed? Explain your answer.

Sketch the trajectory of each ball, then answer the question in the space opposite.

EXAM QUESTION 2

(a) A long-jumper takes off at an angle of 25° above the horizontal. If their take-off speed is 10.5 m s⁻¹, how long will their jump be?

Sketch the jumper's initial trajectory, resolve their speed into horizontal and vertical components and solve the problem.

(b) What would be the jumper's range if they could achieve a 45° take-off with the same launch speed?

Newton's laws of motion

When it comes to mechanics, Newton's laws are the absolute essentials.

○○○

NEWTON'S FIRST LAW OF MOTION

Write Newton's first law of motion in your own words.

What is inertia?

DON'T FORGET
Balanced forces imply constant velocity, and constant velocity implies balanced forces.

A cyclist exerts a forward force of 300 N and travels at a constant speed along a straight road. What can you say about the forces resisting the cyclist's motion?

If the cyclist increases the forwards force to 400 N, what will happen?

NEWTON'S SECOND LAW OF MOTION   ○○○

DON'T FORGET
Acceleration is the clue that tells you forces are unbalanced.

This law describes the effect of an unbalanced force on a body's motion. Write it as an equation relating force, mass and acceleration.

What can you say about the directions of force and acceleration?

If the cyclist's mass is 50 kg, what is their initial acceleration when they raise the forward force from 300 N to 400 N?

NEWTON'S THIRD LAW OF MOTION   ○○○

Write Newton's third law of motion here.

Why can action and reaction forces never balance each other?

WATCH OUT
Action and reaction are always the same sort of force (both are contact forces, both are gravitational forces, etc.) and they act on different bodies.

Give some examples of action and reaction pairs.

Turn the page for some exam questions on this topic ➤

EXAM QUESTION 1 ○○○

(a) State in words Newton's second law of motion.

(b) Explain how the newton is defined.

(c) Describe, with the aid of diagrams, an experiment you could carry out to verify Newton's second law.

EXAM QUESTION 2 ○○○

(a) A certain car can apply a maximum braking force of 2500 N.

Calculate its braking distance when travelling at 20 m s^{-1} if the combined mass of the car and its driver is 500 kg.

(b) Fully loaded with passengers and luggage, the car is 50% heavier. What is its loaded braking distance?

(c) Total stopping distance will normally be greater than this. Why?

Free-body force diagrams

A free-body force diagram should be your starting point in virtually every mechanics problem.

FORCES AND THEIR DIRECTIONS   ○○○

The most common forces in AS level problems are weight, thrust or driving force, friction, drag, lift and the normal reaction. For each of these forces, state the direction.

Fill in the directions.

Force	Direction
Weight	
Driving force	
Friction, drag	
Lift	
Normal reaction	

REVISION EXPRESS
To calculate the normal reaction, you first have to work out the action (i.e. the contact force of the body on the surface). This is often, but not always, equal in size to the component of the body's weight acting at 90° into the surface. See pp. 16–17 of the Revision Express A-level Study Guide.

FREE-BODY FORCE DIAGRAMS   ○○○

A free-body force diagram shows the forces acting on a particular body and nothing else. Draw free-body force diagrams for (a) a block resting on a rough inclined surface; (b) a caravan being towed at a steady speed up a slope; and (c) an aeroplane flying horizontally at a steady speed, banking its wings at an angle of 25° to turn.

Block

Set out the force balance along the surface and normal to the surface.

Caravan

Constant velocity implies balanced forces. Set out the force balance along the slope and normal to the slope.

Aeroplane

Say whether the forces balance vertically and whether they balance horizontally. Write expressions for any force balances or resultant forces.

Turn the page for some exam questions on this topic ➤

EXAM QUESTION 1

● ● ●

A car of mass 750 kg is driven up a 15° hill at a constant velocity. If the car's engines provide a driving force of 5000 N, calculate the size of the combined drag and friction forces acting on the car.

Draw a free-body force diagram. Calculate the car's weight (assume $g = 9.81 \text{ m s}^{-2}$), then solve the problem.

EXAM QUESTION 2

● ● ●

A lift in a skyscraper contains a set of bathroom scales. Passengers can stand on the scales to see what the ride does to their 'weight' (strictly, what it does to the contact force). The lift has a fixed maximum speed, which it reaches quite rapidly.

(a) Describe qualitatively what happens to the reading on the scales as the passenger ascends from the ground floor to the top floor.

There is not enough space here to sketch force diagrams, but you should do them somewhere.

(b) The passenger's mass is 65 kg. What is happening to them when the scales read 40 kg? Be as quantitative as you can.

EXAM QUESTION 3

● ● ●

A mechanic uses a block and tackle to lift a car's engine out of a car. If all pulleys are friction-free and 800 N is the tension in the rope while the engine is held steady, what is the weight of the engine?

Solve this problem by resolving forces horizontally and vertically. The tension in the rope is the same everywhere.

Momentum and impulse

Momentum is the tendency to keep moving steadily. Impulse is the only thing that can alter a body's momentum.

THE LAW OF CONSERVATION OF MOMENTUM   ○○○

The total momentum of any isolated system before any interaction is exactly the same as the total momentum after it. Momentum is conserved in every interaction.

> **Define momentum in words and symbols.**

Word			
Symbol			

When two objects collide, the momentum gained by one equals the momentum lost by the other. For a collision between two bodies, the law of conservation of momentum can be summarized as follows:

> **State the law of conservation of momentum in your own words. Translate your law into a useful equation. Define all terms.**

DON'T FORGET
Momentum is a vector quantity. Choose which direction is positive before you start doing calculations.

Why is momentum conservation often difficult to demonstrate in collisions between trolleys or cars?

IMPULSE   ○○○

Define impulse and say what it causes.

Write the equation linking impulse and momentum.

DON'T FORGET
The units of impulse are the same as the units of momentum.
$1 \, \text{N s} = 1 \, \text{kg m s}^{-1}$.
You must be familiar with both units.

This is a more general version of Newton's second law of motion. It simplifies to $F = ma$ when m and a are constant.
Find the impulse to accelerate a 90 kg go-kart from $10 \, \text{m s}^{-1}$ to $12 \, \text{m s}^{-1}$.

EXAMINER'S SECRETS
The impulse equation provides a way of solving problems involving rockets and jets (the force produced by a constant stream of matter, etc.). These problems regularly crop up in various guises.

A fire hose exerts a force of 80 N on a fire-fighter when a jet of water is pumped out at $20 \, \text{m s}^{-1}$. Calculate flow rate of the water in the jet.

Turn the page for some exam questions on this topic ➤

EXAM QUESTION 1

● ● ●

A train couples up to a stationary truck by shunting into it. The train's mass is 220 tonnes and the truck's mass is 60 tonnes. The train runs into the truck at 0.75 m s^{-1}. Calculate the combined speed of the train and truck after the collision (neglecting friction).

EXAM QUESTION 2

○ ○ ○

A rocket fires out hot exhaust gases at rate 400 kg s^{-1} and at speed 10 km s^{-1} (relative to the rocket). Find the net force on the rocket.

EXAMINER'S SECRETS
Learn this version of the impulse equation. It comes up very often in jet problems.

What will happen to the rocket's rate of acceleration over the next few seconds? Assume the engine's performance remains constant.

EXAM QUESTION 3

● ● ●

An asteroid is heading towards Earth. Its mass is 1.5×10^{13} kg and its velocity is 25 km s^{-1}, directly towards the centre of the Earth.

Calculate the asteroid's momentum.

DON'T FORGET
Inelastic collisions are where the two colliding objects join together. All momentum is shared by the combined body.

Scientists come up with two plans of action. Plan A involves sending a rocket to knock the asteroid off its path. The rocket's maximum mass and speed (on impact) are 2.0×10^4 kg and 1.0×10^7 m s^{-1}.

If the rocket hits the asteroid inelastically when it is 1.5×10^8 m away from the Earth's centre, could the plan work? The Earth's radius is about 6.5×10^6 m.

First decide the direction from which the rocket should hit the asteroid. Calculate the momentum and velocity imparted by the collision. Use the asteroid's speed to calculate the time to expected impact.

Will the asteroid hit or miss?

Plan B is to send a team of experts to land on the asteroid, drill into it, plant a bomb and explode the asteroid into a thousand pieces. What effect will this have on the path of the asteroid's centre of mass?

What effect will it have on the likely Earth impact? Consider best and worst cases.

You have to assume that the full impact would cause worldwide devastation to answer this question.

Which plan wins?

Work, energy and power

Energy transfer drives every process.

WORK

○○○

Work is the transfer of energy. Work is done whenever a force moves an object. Work done is defined by the equation:

> **Write the defining equation in the space provided. Give units.**

> **Now write the formula for a force acting at an angle θ to the object's direction of motion.**

WORK DONE BY A VARIABLE FORCE

○○○

Work done is equal to the area under a force–distance graph.

> **WATCH OUT**
> You must plot force up the y-axis, distance along the x-axis. Work done is the integral of force with respect to distance moved.

What is the formula for work done by a simple spring?

> **LINKS**
> For more information on force, extension and energy in typical solids, see pp. 23–24.

ENERGY CONVERSIONS

○○○

> **WATCH OUT**
> In an isolated system where mechanical energy is conserved, $E_k + E_p$ is constant. If you take the top of a roller coaster ride as $h = 0$, E_p will always be negative, which can cause confusion. Be crystal clear. Write things like: potential energy lost = kinetic energy gained.

Roller coasters, ski slopes, pendulums, projectiles, etc., all provide ideal subjects to test your understanding of energy interconversions. Provided no energy is transferred to the surroundings (e.g. through friction), gravitational potential energy E_p lost = kinetic energy E_k gained (and vice versa). Write down equations for E_p and E_k.

E_p is always a change in energy, not an absolute amount. Explain.

> **EXAMINER'S SECRETS**
> The dependence of kinetic energy on v^2 is a favourite exam theme (and an important safety issue). At AS level, it is likely to be linked to the braking distance.

How does a car's braking distance depend on its speed?

MOTIVE POWER

○○○

> **WATCH OUT**
> The F in the power equation is the driving force, not the net resultant force. The same equation can be used to give braking power.

A vehicle's instantaneous power (its work rate) is equal to the driving force multiplied by the rate of movement, i.e.

Turn the page for some exam questions on this topic ➤

EXAM QUESTION 1 ●●●

A cyclist uses a constant net force of 160 N to accelerate from rest for 8.0 s on a flat road. If the mass of the cyclist plus their bicycle is 80 kg, calculate (a) their final speed, (b) their final kinetic energy, (c) the maximum height of hill they could free-wheel up (ignoring drag and friction).

EXAM QUESTION 2 ●●●

WATCH OUT
Speeds must be in m s^{-1} for all kinetic energy calculations.

(a) Calculate the kinetic energy of a car of total mass (with passengers and luggage) 1080 kg travelling at a speed of 80 km h^{-1}.

(b) The car's brakes provide a total braking force of 1600 N. If this is maintained throughout braking, what is the minimum braking distance?

(c) Calculate the average power dissipated during braking.

DON'T FORGET
Average power is the total amount of work done divided by the total time taken.

(d) What is the maximum power dissipated by the brakes? Why is this answer different from your answer to (c)?

EXAM QUESTION 3 ●●●

The graph shows how a catapult's extension varies with the force applied.

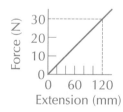

IF YOU HAVE TIME
Try calculating the force needed to propel the same missile at twice the speed.

(a) Calculate the energy stored when the extension is 120 mm.

(b) Estimate the speed the catapult imparts to a 30 g missile.

EXAM QUESTION 4 ●●●

IF YOU HAVE TIME
Calculate the maximum range of the boat assuming it continues travelling at 7 m s^{-1}.
How could the driver increase his range?

A 600 kg powerboat is cruising at a steady 7.0 m s^{-1}. Its engine provides a constant driving force of 800 N. (a) What is the boat's power? (b) The fuel reserves amount to 12 MJ. For how long can the boat carry on at this speed?

Force, extension and energy for solids

Most materials obey Hooke's law within limits, making it one of the most important laws in engineering.

HOOKE'S LAW AND THE BEHAVIOUR OF SIMPLE SPRINGS ○○○

WATCH OUT
Extension is the extra length of the spring, not its total length.

> Sketch the graph carefully. Show where Hooke's law breaks down; mark the elastic limit.

THE JARGON
The elastic limit is the limit beyond which permanent deformation occurs. It is not normally the point at which Hooke's law breaks down.

A spring is stretched to destruction. Sketch its force–extension curve.

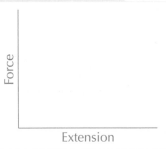

Up to the limit of proportionality, Hooke's law is obeyed.

> Write the symbol equation for Hooke's law.

Note that Hooke's law breaks down before permanent deformation (the elastic limit) is reached.

ENERGY STORED IN A SPRING ○○○

WATCH OUT
The graph is deliberately plotted in an unusual way. Extension depends on force, so extension would normally be plotted up the y-axis. But with force on the y-axis, the gradient of the graph gives the spring constant k and the area under the graph represents the energy stored.

The work done by a variable force is obtained from the area under a force–displacement curve. It is normally equal to the energy stored in the stretched spring.

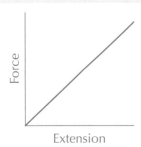

> Shade in the area that gives the energy stored by a simple spring.

Show that the energy stored in a simple spring is given by $E = \frac{1}{2}kx^2$.

HOOKE'S LAW APPLIED TO MATERIALS ○○○

EXAMINER'S SECRETS
Hooke's law for springs is covered at GCSE. It provides a useful introduction to this more general version.

LINKS
For a more detailed look at stress–strain curves, see pp. 25–26.

Within limits, stress is directly proportional to strain. Beyond the limit of proportionality, various strange things may happen.

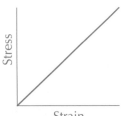

Young's modulus =

Energy density =

> Using the graph, how do you find the Young's modulus and the energy density (energy stored per unit volume) for the material?

> Complete the table.

Quantity	Definition (words)	Symbols	Unit
Stress σ			
Strain ε			
Young's modulus E			

Turn the page for some exam questions on this topic ➤

23

PHYSICS

EXAM QUESTION 1

● ● ●

A certain spring has a spring constant of 0.20 N mm⁻¹. It is held vertically, unstressed. A 5.0 N weight is attached and the spring is released.

(a) What is the maximum distance the ball will fall?

> Use conservation of energy to solve the problem. Be clear about your reasoning.

WATCH OUT
It is easy to make mistakes using intuition alone. When the calculations are simple, there is no excuse for cutting corners.

(b) The spring is cut in half. What is the half-spring's spring constant? If the same weight were attached to the unstressed half-spring, what would be the maximum distance it would fall?

EXAM QUESTION 2

● ● ●

A bow manufacturer makes two types of bow: a simple bow (cheap) and a 'compound bow' (expensive). The graphs show how the force required varies as each bow is drawn towards full extension (0.5 m).

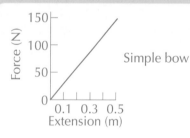
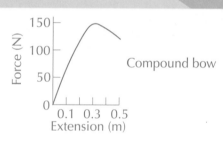

(a) Estimate or calculate the elastic potential energy of each bow at full extension.

(b) What advantage does the compound bow offer?

EXAMINER'S SECRETS
Always convert to SI units before doing long calculations, and check that your answers seem reasonable. Examiners try to make questions realistic. Suppose your answer to 2(c) were 350 m s⁻¹, you should be suspicious because arrows don't generally break the sound barrier.

(c) Estimate the release speed of an arrow of mass 0.060 kg from the simple bow (from the fully extended position) assuming all the bow's elastic energy is transferred to the arrow as kinetic energy.

EXAM QUESTION 3

● ● ●

A nylon fishing line has diameter 0.86 mm and length 1.50 m. If the Young's modulus of nylon is 3.7×10^9 Pa, find the line's extension when it supports a 16 N fish.

Stress and strain

Understanding the behaviour of materials under stress is essential for good engineering and design.

LINKS
For key definitions relevant to force, extension and energy, see pp. 23–24.

REVISION EXPRESS
A basic treatment of stress and strain is given on pp. 26–27 of the Revision Express A-level Study Guide; for more depth and detail, see the Study Guide sections on materials, pp. 164–169.

> Revise key definitions and terms, study the graphs and answer the questions as fully as you can.

THE JARGON
Ultimate tensile stress (UTS) is the greatest stress a material can take before breaking.

THE JARGON
Yield stress is the stress at the elastic limit (where plastic behaviour starts).

THE JARGON
Limit of proportionality is the point where Hooke's law breaks down.

THE JARGON
Ductile flow is plastic behaviour beyond the yield point, where extra stress results in greatly increased strain, due to moving dislocations. Metals exhibit ductile flow.

THE JARGON
Creep is continued ductile flow when no extra stress is added.

TYPICAL STRESS–STRAIN CURVES   ○○○

Stress–strain curves can be used to tell us the Young's modulus of a material, its energy density under stress, strength, flexibility, etc.

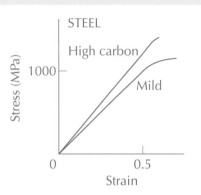 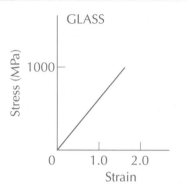

Which features of the steel graph show that high-carbon steel is stronger, stiffer and more brittle than mild steel?

The glass graph shows no plastic behaviour at all. Explain why.

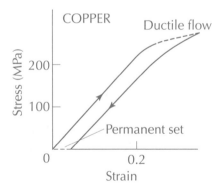 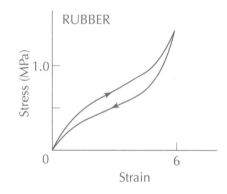

Copper shows 'permanent set' beyond the yield point. Explain.

Rubber is incredibly elastic. Explain why.

The rubber graph also shows that the work done in stretching a rubber band is not equal to the elastic energy the band will repay on release. What happens to the excess energy used and what is the name of this effect?

Turn the page for some exam questions on this topic ➤

EXAM QUESTION 1 ●●●

A stress–strain graph is plotted for a wire stretched to breaking point.

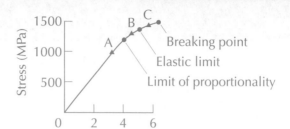

(a) Calculate Young's modulus for the wire. Next find the metal's yield strain. Then find the metal's ultimate tensile stress (UTS).

(b) Describe what would have happened if the stress had been removed at points A, B and C.

(c) Given that the wire's diameter is 1.5 mm and its length is 1.20 m, find the elastic potential energy of the wire at stress 6.0×10^8 Pa.

EXAM QUESTION 2 ●●●

An engineer makes scale model cranes. The crane's lifting cables are made of high-tensile steel with UTS 1.6×10^9 Pa and the loads are solid cubic bricks of density 2000 kg m^{-3}.

(a) Calculate the maximum load each crane can lift.

(b) Work out if each crane can lift its load.

Current as a flow of charge

Current is a flow of charge. In metals the charge carriers are electrons. Metals are good electrical conductors because they have lots of free electrons available to carry charge.

CONDUCTIVITY ○○○

> Materials can be classified according to how well they conduct. Give a definition for insulators, semiconductors and conductors.

> IF YOU HAVE TIME
> Build up a bank of formulae used throughout this section.

Insulators	
Semiconductors	
Conductors	

CURRENT AS A RATE OF FLOW OF CHARGE ○○○

Current (I) and charge (Q) are related by $I = Q/t$ or $Q = It$.

> Use $Q = It$ as a basis to calculate how much charge flowed in the 30 s illustrated by this graph.

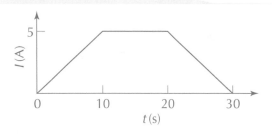

The area under the graph gives the amount of charge that flows.

> Complete these equations.

> THE JARGON
> A rate is a comparison of one quantity with another. In physics, a rate is normally a comparison against time, e.g. acceleration is a comparison of how quickly velocity changes with time.

In the first 10 s	charge	=	
In the middle 10 s	charge	=	
In the last 10 s	charge	=	
Total charge that flowed		=	

CURRENT AND DRIFT VELOCITY ○○○

> Here are some estimates: $n = 10^{29}$ for copper at 20 °C, $A = 8 \times 10^{-7}\,m^2$ say for a wire, $e = -1.6 \times 10^{-19}\,C$ and $v = 1\,mm\,s^{-1}$ typically.

The current I in a metal wire is given by $I = nAev$, where n is the number of electrons per unit volume, A = cross-sectional area, e = charge carried by a free electron, v = drift velocity of free electrons.

SOME COMMON CIRCUIT SYMBOLS ○○○

> Name the circuit component that each symbol represents.

Turn the page for some exam questions on this topic ➤

EXAM QUESTION 1

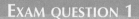

Use the chart to help you begin answering this question.

This chart gives conductivity values for three groups of materials.

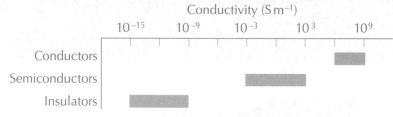

(a) What is the minimum conductivity of a conductor?

(b) What happens to the conductivity of semiconductors with increasing temperature?

(c) Why does the conductivity of semiconductors vary in this way?

EXAM QUESTION 2

A variety of experiments can be used to support the theory that current is a flow of charge, e.g. conduction by coloured salts.

(a) Suggest three other pieces of evidence that support this theory.

LINKS
For Kirchhoff's laws, see pp. 35–36.

(b) Describe an experiment to show conduction by coloured salts.

Draw a diagram to illustrate your answer.

Describe a method, suggest a set of observations and offer a conclusion.

28

PHYSICS

Current, p.d. and resistance

For a current to flow through a conductor, a potential difference (p.d.) must be applied across it. If a conductor with a higher resistance is used, less current will flow for the same p.d.

ENERGY TRANSFERS ○○○

Electrons are joule (jewel) thieves; they transfer precious energy. Use arrows to link each partial statement with the appropriate ending.

IF YOU HAVE TIME
Start to make a list of all the physical quantities used in this topic, together with their symbol and unit.

1	Batteries are a store of	light energy
2	When electrons pick it up, it is then	electrical energy
3	As electrons move, it is considered as	thermal energy
4	Electrons transfer energy to resistors as	chemical energy
5	Light bulbs convert $\leq 5\%$ of energy into	kinetic energy

POTENTIAL DIFFERENCE ○○○

Identify each of the correct statements in this list with a T for true or an F for false.

WATCH OUT
Don't confuse the definition of the volt ($1\,V = 1\,J\,C^{-1}$) and the definition of the amp ($1\,A = 1\,C\,s^{-1}$).

Potential difference (p.d.) is the scientific name for voltage ☐

Potential difference is measured in volts (V) where $1\,V = 1\,J\,C^{-1}$ ☐

Potential difference is measured using a voltmeter in series ☐

The potential difference between two points is the electrical energy converted into other forms when 1 C of charge passes between them ☐

The potential differences across bulbs in parallel add up to the potential difference of their supply ☐

The potential difference between two points is the energy transferred in moving $+1\,C$ of charge between them ☐

SERIES AND PARALLEL CIRCUITS ○○○

Electrical components can be connected in series or parallel. Write down whether each statement is true for series circuits only, for parallel circuits only, or for both types of circuit.

Electrons give up all their energy before returning to the power supply

The current is the same at every point

There must be at least one complete path to allow current to flow

The electrons have more than one possible route available to them

Turn the page for some exam questions on this topic ➤

For more on this topic, see pages 62–63 of the *Revision Express A-level Study Guide*

EXAM QUESTION 1   ● ● ●

This circuit contains four identical lamps. (a) Which lamps will be the brightest?
(b) Which lamps will have the greatest current flowing through them? (c) What
type of meter is X? (d) Add an arrow to the diagram to show the direction in
which conventional current leaves the battery. Label this arrow C.

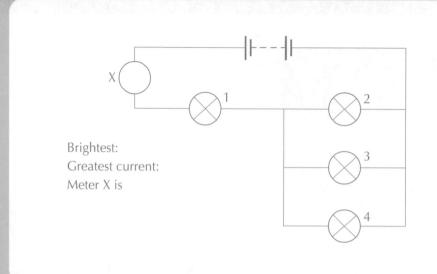

Brightest:
Greatest current:
Meter X is

EXAM QUESTION 2   ● ● ●

WATCH OUT
This question uses the term 'voltage', now considered vague and old-fashioned. Use p.d. and e.m.f. as a way to clarify the meaning of voltage in your answer.

The **resistance** of a component tells us about how much **current** will flow
through it for a given **voltage**.

Define then explain the physical origins of the words in bold.

Complete this table.

	Symbol	Equation	Unit	Unit definition
Resistance				
Current				
Voltage				

Fill in the missing labels on this diagram.

Give a short explanation of the physical origin of each of these terms.

Resistance

Current

Voltage

EXAMINER'S SECRETS
Electromotive force is really a misnomer. It is not a force at all. It describes an energy change where energy is transferred to charge.

30
PHYSICS

© Pearson Education Limited 2001

Resistors and resistivity

The resistance of a wire indicates how hard it is for electrons to flow through it. Length, cross-sectional area, temperature and material all affect resistance.

OHM'S LAW ○○○

The current through a conductor is proportional to the p.d. across it, provided the temperature of the conductor remains constant.

> Rearrange $V = IR$ to make R the subject of the equation, then complete the table of results for this experiment.

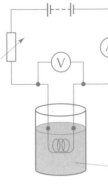

p.d. (V)	I (A)	R (Ω)
2.0	0.5	
4.0	1.0	
6.0	1.5	

Water to keep the wire at a constant temperature

> Answer these questions to reach the conclusion for this experiment.

For each set of measurements quoted above, what can you say about potential difference divided by current?

If p.d. doubles then what happens to I?

How are I and p.d. related?

FACTORS AFFECTING RESISTANCE ○○○

The results of the previous experiment have been plotted in the following graph and labelled A.

> Label both axes on this graph.

> Add a second line to show a set of results that might be obtained from a wire of greater resistance; label this line B.

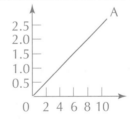

> Note the equation that shows the factors affecting the resistance of a wire at constant temperature.

The resistances of two different wires are not always the same.

RESISTORS IN SERIES AND PARALLEL ○○○

> Redraw this circuit to show more clearly how to construct it in practice. Then calculate R_{total} (R_t) if $R_1 = R_2 = 4\,\Omega$.

Series: $R_{total} = R_1 + R_2 + R_3$ Parallel: $1/R_{total} = 1/R_1 + 1/R_2 + 1/R_3$

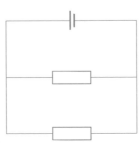

Turn the page for some exam questions on this topic ➤

EXAM QUESTION 1   ○○○

The resistance of a thermistor varies with temperature.

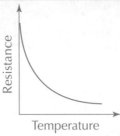

(a) Describe the relationship illustrated by this graph.

(b) Thermistors are non-ohmic. Describe what this means and give two other examples of non-ohmic electrical components.

(c) Sketch a graph to show how the p.d. across a thermistor varies with the current I through it.

WATCH OUT
Read questions carefully. If you're asked to plot a graph of I against p.d., I should be on the y-axis and p.d. should be on the x-axis.

EXAM QUESTION 2   ○○○

A student is asked to determine the resistivity of a 20 cm long pencil lead (a compound of graphite and clay). They are then required to calculate the thickness of a pencil line drawn with this pencil lead.

(a) The student sharpened both ends of the pencil and found that the resistance of the lead was 5.1×10^{-3} Ω. If the diameter of the lead was 2.00 mm, what was its resistivity?

DON'T FORGET
Show your method whenever you do a calculation.

(b) The student used the pencil to draw a uniformly thick line, 30 cm long and 2 mm wide. Using an ohmmeter, they found the line to have a resistance of 600 Ω. What was the thickness of the pencil line?

EXAMINER'S SECRETS
Marks are often allocated for units, so don't forget to state them in your final answer.

32

PHYSICS

Electrical energy and power

Electricity can be used to transfer energy. Electrons are used to 'pick up' and 'drop off' packets of energy. Power tells us how quickly energy is changed from one form to another.

THE JARGON
A complete circuit has two parts: the internal circuit (inside the power supply) and the external circuit (bulbs, resistors, etc.).

Give an example of these energy transfers.

ENERGY TRANSFORMATIONS   ○○○

In complete circuits, energy changes occur in the power supply or in the external circuit.

In the power supply

In the external circuit

POWER EQUATION $P = VI$ ○○○

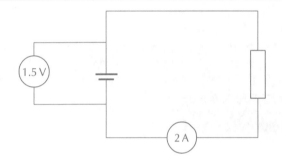

Complete these statements to explain why $P = VI$.

1 V is defined as

Here each coulomb of charge entering the cell gains

1 A is defined as

Here the number of coulombs entering and leaving the cell every second is

SYLLABUS CHECK
Some courses expect you to be able to check that equations are homogeneous. If this is so for your course, check $P = VI$ and $P = I^2R$.

Power is defined as

As 2×1.5 J leave the cell every second, the power is

THE JARGON
Dissipate means to scatter. Energy changes in an external circuit usually involve heating, so they are irreversible. Therefore 'dissipate' is a good word to use.

POWER DISSIPATED $P = I^2R$ ○○○

Statement	True/false	Correction (if needed)
$P = VI$ is used for power gains		
To transmit at high power, use high V or low I		
$P = I^2R$ is used for energy losses		
When transmitting at high power it does not matter whether V or I is large		
It's not possible to transmit at high power and minimize power losses		

Complete this table to see how electricity is transmitted by the national grid.

DON'T FORGET
$P = VI$ can be used when power is lost or gained by electrons. $P = I^2R$ is only used when electrons lose power.

Turn the page for some exam questions on this topic ➤

EXAM QUESTION 1

●●●

The cell below has negligible internal resistance and the bulbs are identical.

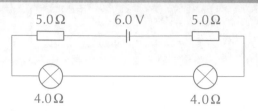

5.0 Ω   6.0 V   5.0 Ω

4.0 Ω   4.0 Ω

(a) Calculate the current flowing through each bulb.

(b) Calculate the power dissipated in each bulb.

(c) Calculate the amount of energy changed into other forms by each bulb in 2.0 minutes.

EXAM QUESTION 2

●●●

Highlight the most important parts of this paragraph.

'Quick blow' fuses are used to protect a variety of delicate electrical devices. You are asked to test one such fuse to check its maker's claim that it blows within 5 ms of the current rising above 3 A. Design an experiment to carry out this task.

Why are these parts significant?

Draw a circuit diagram of your experiment.

Describe your method and how you would use your results to reach a conclusion.

IF YOU HAVE TIME
Rewrite this answer using a different method, e.g. by using an oscilloscope (CRO) or high-speed photography. Remember to consider the CRO's time base or the camera's shutter speed in your answers.

Kirchhoff's laws

Kirchhoff's laws allow current and voltage to be calculated at any point in a circuit. They are consequences of conservation of charge and energy within electrical circuits.

KIRCHHOFF'S FIRST LAW ○○○

Kirchhoff's first law says that the (algebraic) sum of the currents into a point equals the (algebraic) sum of the currents out of that point. Use Kirchhoff's first law to calculate the currents B, C, D and E.

THE JARGON
Here the word 'algebraic' means that the directions of the currents have to be taken into account.

10 A $B = ?$

$B =$

$10\,A$ $E = ?$ $2\,A$

$E =$

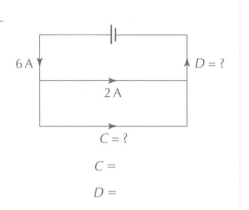

$6\,A$ $D = ?$

$2\,A$

$C = ?$

$C =$

$D =$

KIRCHHOFF'S SECOND LAW ○○○

Kirchhoff's second law says that the (algebraic) sum of the e.m.f.s in any closed loop in a circuit is equal to the (algebraic) sum of the p.d.s around that loop.

SYLLABUS CHECK
Kirchhoff's second law is not required by CCEA.

SYLLABUS CHECK
Check whether your course will set questions involving the use of simultaneous equations.

Complete this calculation.

$\Sigma E = \Sigma IR$ is a mathematical expression of Kirchhoff's second law.

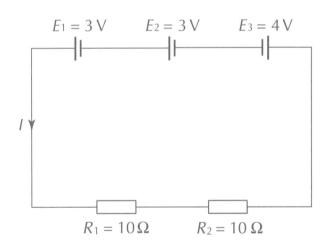

$E_1 = 3\,V$ $E_2 = 3\,V$ $E_3 = 4\,V$

I

$R_1 = 10\,\Omega$ $R_2 = 10\,\Omega$

$\Sigma E = 3 + \quad\quad + \quad\quad = \quad V$

$\Sigma IR = 10I + \quad\quad = \quad V$

$\Sigma E = \Sigma IR \Rightarrow \quad = \quad$ so $I = \quad A$

CONSERVATION LAWS ○○○

Shade to form complete sentences that match Kirchhoff's laws.

LINKS
For more on e.m.f., see pp. 39–40.

| Kirchhoff's first law is a consequence of ... | conservation of energy because ... | electrons do not disappear. |
| Kirchhoff's second law is a consequence of ... | conservation of charge because ... | energy gained by the electrons from the power supplies is lost in the resistors. |

Turn the page for some exam questions on this topic ➤

EXAM QUESTION 1 ●●●

Use Kirchhoff's first law to find values for the currents *a* to *g*.

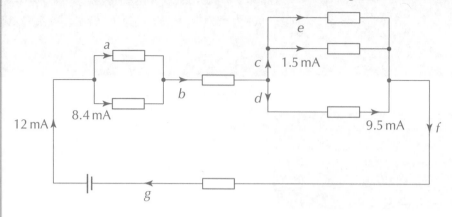

EXAM QUESTION 2 ●●●

Use Kirchhoff's first law (K1) and Kirchhoff's second law (K2) to calculate values for I_1, I_2 and I_3.

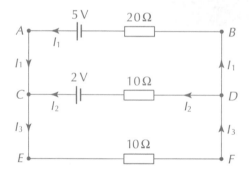

WATCH OUT

You are often asked to put in your own arrows to show current direction. If at the end of your calculation one of your values for current is a negative number, the minus sign indicates that the current flowed in the opposite direction to the way you guessed.

SYLLABUS CHECK

Questions like this are not set by all boards, e.g. AQA:A and AQA:B. The solution to this type of question involves the use of simultaneous equations.

Potential dividers and their uses

The term 'potential divider' describes a circuit in which resistors divide a battery's voltage. Potential dividers are often used with transistors to form electronic control circuits.

PRINCIPLE OF POTENTIAL DIVIDERS   ○○○

WATCH OUT
The term 'potential divider' is a little misleading. Perhaps 'potential difference divider' would more accurately describe these circuits.

THE JARGON
The term 'potentiometer' can be used to describe an instrument for measuring p.d. or e.m.f. It can also refer to a variable resistor (as shown in circuit 2) that can be used to tap off a variable p.d.

> Potential dividers can portion off a small voltage from a larger one. Use this formula to calculate V_{out}.

IF YOU HAVE TIME
Redraw circuit 3 replacing the constantan resistance wire with a number of resistors in series. Then you should be able to see how V_{out} can be varied.

> Potential dividers often form the heart of automatic control circuits. If circuit 2 were to be used in this way, what advantages and limitations would it have? Jot down some ideas in the table opposite.

Circuit 1

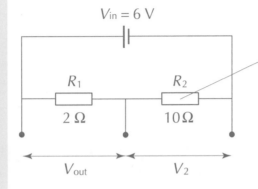

$V_{in} = 6$ V

V_{out} can be altered if a variable resistor is used as R_2

$$V_{out} = V_{in} R_1 / (R_1 + R_2) =$$

Circuit 2   Circuit 3

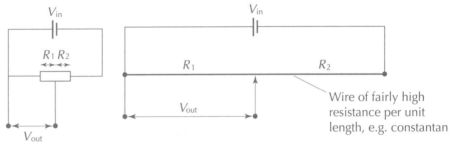

Wire of fairly high resistance per unit length, e.g. constantan

Advantages	Limitations and drawbacks

REAL USES OF POTENTIAL DIVIDERS   ○○○

> List some practical uses of potential dividers.

Turn the page for some exam questions on this topic ➤

EXAM QUESTION 1

The thermistor used in this circuit has a resistance of 1000 Ω at 20 °C. Its resistance falls to 350 Ω when it is heated to 60 °C. Calculate V_{out} at 20 °C and 60 °C.

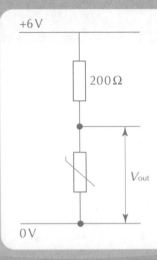

IF YOU HAVE TIME
Test yourself on prefixes: centi, kilo, mega, etc. How many can you remember and explain correctly?

EXAM QUESTION 2

THE JARGON
Rheostat is another name for a variable resistor.

A student used a small value rheostat, connected as shown, to plot an *I–V* characteristic graph for an LED.

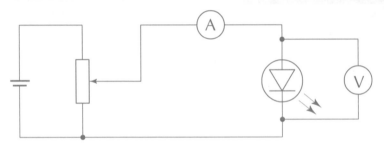

(a) What are the advantages of this arrangement over connecting the rheostat in series with the ammeter?

(b) Why might the student's choice of a small value rheostat be a problem in the circuit that has been constructed?

WATCH OUT
Say 'a small value rheostat', not 'a small rheostat'. A rheostat that provides relatively small resistances may not necessarily have a small volume.

EXAM QUESTION 3

Explain how a potential divider could be used in a real-life application of your choice (e.g. as part of a car's fuel gauge).

e.m.f. and internal resistance

Electromotive force is the energy available per unit charge to produce current. Internal resistance is the resistance provided by a source of e.m.f. as charge passes through it.

SYLLABUS CHECK
CCEA does not require details of cells and measurement of internal resistance.

IF YOU HAVE TIME
Compile a glossary of key scientific words used in this section. Try to limit each explanation to one sentence.

ELECTROMOTIVE FORCE

○○○

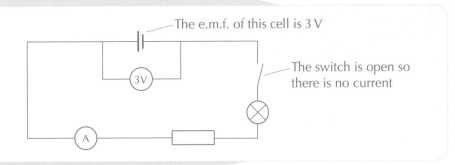

The e.m.f. of this cell is 3 V

The switch is open so there is no current

INTERNAL RESISTANCE

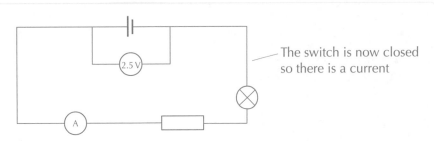

The switch is now closed so there is a current

The electrons pick up energy as they pass through the cell, but the chemicals in the cell also provide some internal resistance.

Sketch a more advanced symbol for a cell showing that cells provide internal resistance. Use this symbol from now on whenever a cell is assumed to have internal resistance.

Complete this table.

Simple symbol	Advanced symbol

Source of e.m.f.	Internal resistance caused by
Cell (or battery of cells)	
Power pack (transformer)	

Complete this example to calculate the current flowing in the circuit and the reading on the voltmeter.

R_{total} = $R_1 + R_2 = R + r$

=

$V = IR$ so $I = V/R$

Here $I = E/(R + r)$

so $I =$

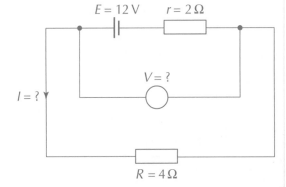

$E = 12$ V $r = 2\,\Omega$

$V = ?$

$I = ?$

$R = 4\,\Omega$

DON'T FORGET
Note that r causes terminal p.d. to drop when there is a current.

p.d. across cell terminals = p.d. across resistor R

V = IR (for resistor R) =

Turn the page for some exam questions on this topic ➤

EXAM QUESTION 1 ○○○

A friend has been absent for several lessons and asks you to explain the main effects of 'internal resistance'.

WATCH OUT
The terminal p.d. (i.e. the p.d. across the terminals of the cell) equals the p.d. across the external resistors, not the 'lost volts' across the internal resistance of the cell.

EXAM QUESTION 2 ○○○

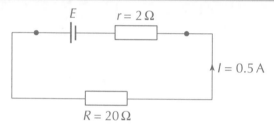

(a) Calculate the 'lost volts', the cell's terminal p.d. and its e.m.f.

DON'T FORGET
The terminal p.d. of a cell is equal to its e.m.f. only when no current is flowing.

(b) Describe qualitatively how this circuit could be changed to make the terminal p.d. have a value closer to the e.m.f. of the cell.

(c) Why would your change in part (b) have the desired effect?

(d) What kind of voltmeter should be used to measure the e.m.f. of a power supply? Explain your answer.

Types of waves and their properties

Waves are vibrations that carry energy. Some waves, e.g. sound, need a medium to travel through; others, e.g. light, do not. Waves never involve an overall movement of matter.

CLASSIFYING WAVES: SIX TERMS ○○○

Jot down some notes about each type of wave shown here.

IF YOU HAVE TIME
Illustrate each wave type with an example.

SPEED LEARNING
Use a mnemonic to remember different wave types: **P**erry **M**ason **s**olves **l**egal **t**angles **e**asily (progressive, mechanical, stationary, longitudinal, transverse, electromagnetic).

Wave classification	Notes
Transverse	
Longitudinal	
Mechanical	
Electromagnetic	
Progressive	
Stationary or standing	

DESCRIBING WAVES ○○○

This diagram represents a side-on view of a transverse wave. Add some labels.

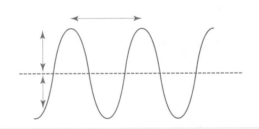

Add arrows to this table to match each term with the correct definition. Write the correct unit in the right-hand column. The unit for speed has been entered for you.

	Term	Definition or equation	Unit
1	Frequency	Time for one complete vibration	
2	Amplitude	Number of vibrations per second	
3	Period	Maximum displacement	
4	Displacement	Distance between point on wave and line of zero disturbance	
5	Wavelength	Frequency × wavelength	
6	Speed	Distance between two adjacent points that are in phase	m s^{-1}

WAVE EQUATION ○○○

The wave equation is $v = f\lambda$. A wave travels at speed $v = 0.40\ \mathrm{m\ s^{-1}}$, and its frequency is $f = 5.0\ \mathrm{Hz}$. What is its wavelength λ?

Turn the page for some exam questions on this topic ➤

41

PHYSICS

EXAM QUESTION 1

○○○

(a) Explain the meaning of mechanical transverse and mechanical longitudinal waves.

(b) Give one example of each type of wave in part (a).

(c) What is meant by polarization?

This is a tricky question; try to base your answer on a simple demonstration.

(d) Why is it that only transverse waves and not longitudinal waves can be polarized? Illustrate your answer with diagrams if possible.

EXAMINER'S SECRETS
As the question suggests using a diagram, some marks may only be obtainable this way. In other words, do a diagram or lose marks.

EXAM QUESTION 2

○○○

SYLLABUS CHECK
AQA:A uses multiple choice questions. Check the types of question set by your exam board.

Circle the letter beside the one statement that is incorrect.

All waves carry energy	A
Electromagnetic waves can be polarized	B
Only transverse waves can be diffracted	C
Waves propagate by progressive local displacement of a medium or a change in its physical properties	D

Reflection and refraction

When waves or particles are reflected, the angle of incidence equals the angle of reflection. Waves refract (change direction) if they change speed when entering a new medium at a slanting angle.

THE LAWS OF REFLECTION

Label the diagram, then sketch the results that would be obtained. Use the graph provided.

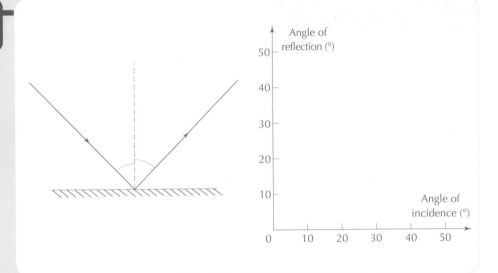

Make a note of the laws of reflection.

THE LAWS OF REFRACTION

(a) refractive index $_1n_2 = \dfrac{\text{speed of light in medium 1}}{\text{speed of light in medium 2}}$

IF YOU HAVE TIME
Find out about the travelling microscope and how it can be used to determine the refractive index of a glass block.

(b) $n_1 = \dfrac{\text{speed of light in a vacuum}}{\text{speed of light in medium 1}}$

(c) $_1n_2 = \dfrac{\sin i}{\sin r}$

(d) $_1n_2 = \dfrac{\text{real depth}}{\text{apparent depth}}$

(e) $_1n_2 = n_2/n_1$

(f) $_2n_1 = 1/_1n_2$

Choose from (a)–(f) to answer these two questions.

Which law is used to calculate the absolute refractive index?

Which law is named after Willebrod Snell?

This diagram shows a ray of light entering glycerol from air. Complete the calculation to find the refractive index of glycerol:

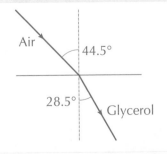

Air   44.5°

28.5°   Glycerol

$_1n_2 = \dfrac{\sin i}{\sin r} = \qquad\qquad =$

Turn the page for some exam questions on this topic ➤

EXAM QUESTION 1

○○○ ●

Using a wavefront diagram, explain why refraction occurs when light enters an optically denser medium at an angle other than 90°.

WATCH OUT
Optical density has nothing to do with mass/volume.

Sketch and label a wavefront diagram to provide your answer.

EXAM QUESTION 2

○○○ ●

SYLLABUS CHECK
Some courses, e.g. OCR:B, expect you to interpret physics that is new to you. Some exams, e.g. some set by AQA:B, include questions based on a scientific passage.

Ultrasound imaging can be used to measure the precise depth of a structure within the body, e.g. the position of the midline of the brain. Each peak (1–4) in this CRO trace shows the position of a reflecting surface. The height of each peak represents the amplitude of the echo received.

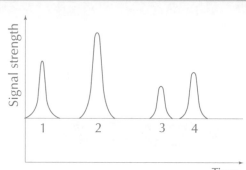

(a) Which peak corresponds to the deepest structure? Say why.

(b) Which peak corresponds to the most reflective surface? Say why.

(c) Can ultrasound be refracted? Give a reason for your answer.

EXAM QUESTION 3

○○○ ●

The refractive index for light travelling between air and diamond is taken to be 2.42.

If a light ray enters diamond at an angle of 30.0°, calculate the angle of refraction.

Show your method clearly.

What is the refractive index for light escaping from diamond into air?

Total internal reflection and fibre optics

Fibre optics are sometimes called 'light pipes'. Light is trapped within them, bouncing along by total internal reflection (TIR). They can convey information encoded as flashes of light.

IF YOU HAVE TIME
Examiners are influenced in the choice of question they set by events or articles reported in the media. Make a habit of keeping up to date yourself.

> Add rays to each of these diagrams to illustrate refraction, the critical angle and total internal reflection.

TOTAL INTERNAL REFLECTION AND THE CRITICAL ANGLE ○○○

The critical angle C is the angle of incidence i that produces an angle of refraction equal to 90°. If $i > C$ the ray is totally internally reflected.

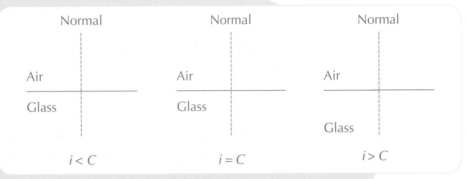

Normal	Normal	Normal
Air	Air	Air
Glass	Glass	Glass
$i < C$	$i = C$	$i > C$

The refractive index of borosilicate is 1.474. To find the critical angle for a ray of light in borosilicate, start with $n = 1/\sin C$.

> Complete the calculation.

FIBRE OPTICS ○○○

Fibre optics use the principle of TIR in a variety of applications.

> List some uses of fibre optics.

Fibre optics have many advantages.

> Now list some advantages.

Fibre optics rely on total internal reflection.

> Label this diagram.

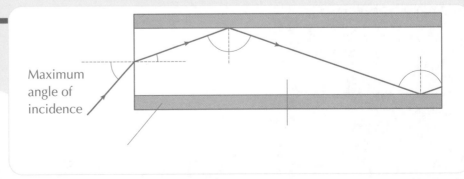

Maximum angle of incidence

CHECK THE NET
If you're interested in how things work, then why not ask a professor of physics? Go to
http://landau1.phys.virginia.edu/Education/Teaching/HowThingsWork

Turn the page for some exam questions on this topic ➤

EXAM QUESTION 1 ○○○

A prism is made from light flint glass of refractive index 1.578.

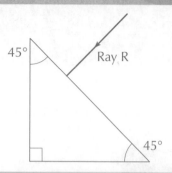

45°   Ray R

45°

(a) Calculate the critical angle for a ray of light in this material.

(b) Use your answer to part (a) to complete the path of ray R through the prism. Show your answer on the diagram above.

(c) Explain why refractive indices do not have units.

EXAM QUESTION 2 ○○○

Describe an experiment to measure the critical angle for light at a Perspex–air boundary.

> Draw a labelled diagram.

> Explain the method and describe what you expect to happen. Finally, show how you will use your results to find the value of *C*.

EXAMINER'S SECRETS
There may be only four marks available for question 2 (one for the apparatus, two for the method and one for your analysis). Use the number of marks available to determine how long you spend on each question.

46

Diffraction

Diffraction is the spreading out of a wave as it passes through a gap or around an obstacle.

GAP WIDTH, WAVELENGTH AND DIFFRACTION   ○○○

The extent to which waves are diffracted depends upon their wavelength and the width of the gap they are passing through.

Complete these wavefront diagrams to show what happens in the spaces beyond the gaps.

IF YOU HAVE TIME
Start to make your own revision cards on the following wave properties: reflection, refraction, diffraction and interference.

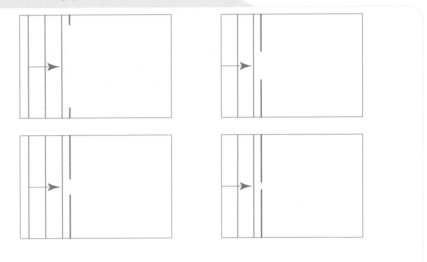

What can be concluded from the diagrams?

SINGLE-SLIT DIFFRACTION OF LIGHT WAVES   ○○○

A very narrow slit can be used to diffract monochromatic laser light.

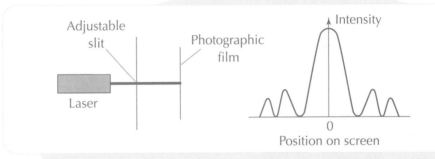

The diffracted light was captured on a photographic film. An analysis of this film is shown above. Position 0 was directly ahead of the slit.

Study the graph and write down any conclusions you can draw from it.

DIFFRACTION OF MICROWAVES   ○○○

The microwaves in this demonstration have a wavelength of 4 cm. Add labels to this diagram.

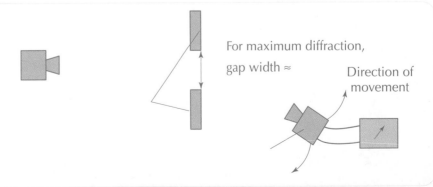

For maximum diffraction, gap width ≈

Direction of movement

Turn the page for some exam questions on this topic ➤

EXAM QUESTION 1

● ● ●

(a) Use a diagram to explain what is meant by diffraction.

(b) A classroom door has been left open. The diagram shows the positions of a quiet student in the classroom and a teacher talking outside. Use your knowledge of diffraction to explain why the student can hear but not see the teacher.

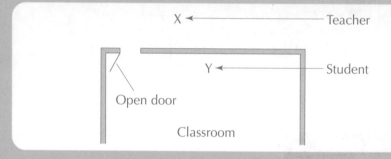

EXAM QUESTION 2

● ● ●

How could you show that the degree of water wave diffraction depends upon the relative sizes of gap width and wavelength?

LINKS
To see a diagram of the equipment used in this experiment, see p. 51.

Superposition

Superposition means placing one figure upon another. The principle of superposition can be applied to all waves and was used by Christian Huygens to support his wave theory of light.

THE PRINCIPLE OF SUPERPOSITION   ○○○

When waves cross, the total displacement at a point equals the sum of the individual displacements at that point.

Complete these flow diagrams to show how crests and troughs form supercrests and supertroughs or cancel to zero.

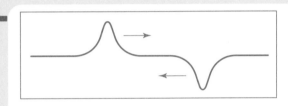

+   →   supercrest

+   →   supertrough

+   →   zero

Complete the diagrams to show the result of each superposition.

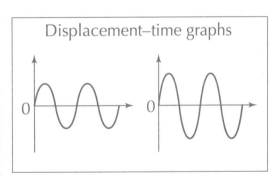

DON'T FORGET
Super revision depends upon the magic five. You should repeat your learning five times: within an hour, a day, a week, a month and then after three months.

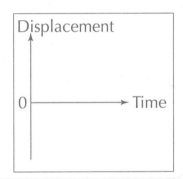

Displacement–time graphs

Displacement

0   → Time

KEY TERMS   ○○○

Explain each of these terms.

In phase	
In antiphase	
Path difference	
Bright fringe	
Dark fringe	

Turn the page for some exam questions on this topic ➤

EXAM QUESTION 1

●●●

(a) 'The *superposition* of light waves from *coherent* sources can produce interference effects.' Explain the words in italics.

> There is no need to use diagrams here.

(b) Is it possible to superpose two waves of different wavelengths to produce an interference pattern? Include diagrams in your answer.

> You need some diagrams here.

EXAMINER'S SECRETS
Many exam questions contain clues. Read the whole question and find the clues.

EXAM QUESTION 2

●●●

(a) 'Superposition involves vector addition.' Explain this statement.

IF YOU HAVE TIME
List some other practical applications of superposition.

(b) State one practical application of superposition.

(c) Look at the diagram, then add to it the wave that would be produced by superposition of the two original waves.

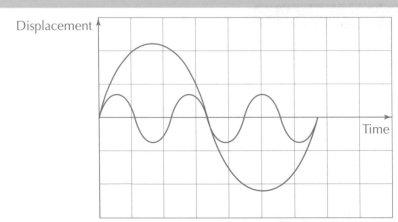

Interference

Interference occurs when waves combine by superposition. The result of interference is an observable pattern if there is a constant phase difference between waves of similar amplitude.

USING A RIPPLE TANK TO OBSERVE INTERFERENCE ○○○

Add labels to this diagram.

EXAMINER'S SECRETS
Try to include details that show you have actually performed the experiment, e.g. an absorber to cut down unwanted reflections from the walls of the ripple tank.

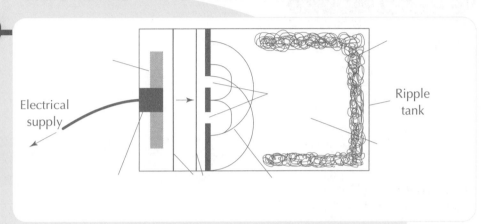

Electrical supply

Ripple tank

List two other pieces of equipment often used with the ripple tank. Explain their functions.

Apparatus	Use

YOUNG'S DOUBLE-SLIT EXPERIMENT – UPDATED ○○○

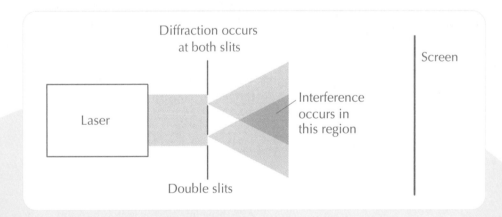

Diffraction occurs at both slits

Screen

Laser

Interference occurs in this region

Double slits

Note the reasons for using a laser.

A laser is used for two main reasons	(1)
	(2)

Note the two main conclusions.

There are two main conclusions	(1)
	(2)

Turn the page for some exam questions on this topic ➤

EXAM QUESTION 1 ●●●

In a Young's double-slit experiment, light of wavelength 0.54×10^{-6} m was incident upon a pair of parallel slits of separation 0.50 mm. The fringes were viewed on a screen that was 90 cm from the slits. Calculate the distance between consecutive bright fringes.

> Write down the correct formula, show your working and highlight your answer.

EXAM QUESTION 2 ●●●

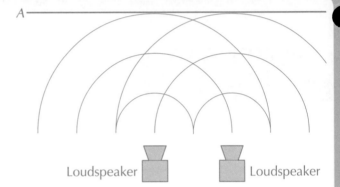

This diagram shows a way to study interference of sound waves.

(a) Assuming that an interference pattern was established, what would you notice if you walked along the line *AB*?

(b) What is constructive interference and how could you recognize a region formed by constructive interference?

(c) Add three lines to the diagram to show where constructive interference occurs.

(d) What is the name given to the semicircular lines in the diagram and what do they indicate?

(e) Suggest two sets of equipment that could be used to detect loud and quiet regions in an experiment such as this.

EXAMINER'S SECRETS
AS questions tend to be qualitative (you have to describe something) whereas A2 questions tend to be more quantitative (you have to calculate something).

IF YOU HAVE TIME
Compile a concept map to summarize the material you have covered in this section.

Standing waves

Standing waves occur when two waves of equal wavelength and amplitude and travelling in opposite directions cross and combine by superposition.

EXPLAINING STANDING WAVES ○○○

The diagrams show two waves travelling in opposite directions. The initial situation is shown in part (a). Subsequent moments are shown in parts (b), (c) and (d).

> Add arrows to (c) and (d) showing how the two waves continue to move in opposite directions.

> Consider the line labelled A. It shows the position of an antinode, where the amplitude of the combined wave varies a lot. Draw another line, to the right of this one, showing the position of the next antinode.

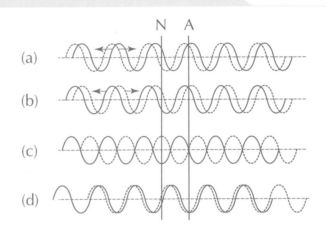

(a)

(b)

(c)

(d)

> Complete these sentences.

IF YOU HAVE TIME
Look again at the first three sentences then write similar ones for the points labelled A.

At all points labelled N, the waves interfere

The combined amplitude at these points is always

These points are called

The positions of nodes (and antinodes) always remain

Adjacent nodes (or adjacent antinodes) are separated by

STANDING WAVE PATTERNS ○○○

Standing waves, or stationary waves, are often demonstrated with sound waves, microwaves or stretched strings as shown here.

> Draw the next two possible standing wave patterns. Include arrows to show the direction of movement of adjacent sections of the strings.

Fundamental frequency or first harmonic   ←—— $\lambda/2$ ——→

First overtone or second harmonic   ←———— λ ————→

Second overtone or third harmonic   ←———— $3\lambda/2$ ————→

> Complete these sentences.

The fixed points at the ends of the string are always

Adjacent nodes are separated by

Adjacent sections of the string move in opposite

Turn the page for some exam questions on this topic ➤

EXAM QUESTION 1

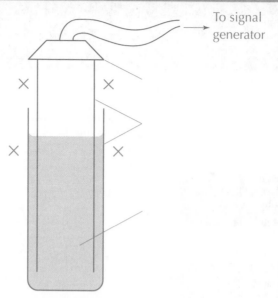

To signal generator

This apparatus was used to investigate standing waves.

(a) Add the missing labels to the diagram.
(b) How would you find the first position at which resonance occurs?

(c) Why is a loud sound generated here?

(d) How does the length of the air column, contained in the inner tube at this position, compare with the wavelength of the sound?

(e) The inner tube is raised and the loudness of the sound changes. How far is the tube raised before the sound reaches its loudest level again? Quote your answer as a fraction of λ.

EXAM QUESTION 2

Two microwave transmitters, producing waves of the same wavelength and frequency, are set up facing each other about 1.0 m apart. A receiver is moved around in the region between them and it is found that points of minimum intensity are separated by 1.4 cm. Calculate the wavelength and frequency of the microwaves. Assume the speed of electromagnetic waves, $c = 3.0 \times 10^8$ m s^{-1}.

Planck's constant

Classical physics could not explain how very hot objects emit radiation or why electrons do not spiral into the nucleus. The work of Max Planck held the key to a new, quantum era.

THE JARGON
Classical physics can be thought of as nineteenth-century physics.

> List four things that classical physics cannot explain.

LIMITATIONS OF CLASSICAL PHYSICS ○○○

THE ULTRAVIOLET CATASTROPHE ○○○

One classical law that couldn't withstand close scrutiny was the Rayleigh–Jeans law. This related the intensity I of electromagnetic radiation, at wavelength λ, to the temperature T of a black body. It suggested that if temperature remains constant then $I \propto 1/\lambda^4$.

THE JARGON
A black body is a perfect emitter and absorber of electromagnetic radiation. Stars are black bodies.

> Plot two graphs on the axes provided, one showing how intensity really varies with wavelength and one showing the trend predicted by Rayleigh–Jeans.

Intensity

0   Wavelength

> Compare the graphs you have drawn. Now complete these conclusions.

The Rayleigh–Jeans law worked only at

Rayleigh–Jeans did not predict

The catastrophe was that

THE JARGON
An empirical expression is obtained from experiment and observation, instead of from theory.

MAX PLANCK'S SOLUTION ○○○

> Planck knew that standing wave patterns could be established on vibrating strings only at certain frequencies. Sketch the three most basic patterns.

Planck explained how black bodies emit electromagnetic (EM) radiation by studying the observed spectrum and producing an expression that agreed with it.

$3f$

$2f$

f

> Planck's idea suggested that the energy of an oscillator comes in whole number multiples of hf. Sketch these quantized energy levels.

Planck suggested that charged particles also can vibrate only at certain frequencies (to emit EM radiation). He suggested that the energy of an oscillator is proportional to its frequency, giving $E = hf$.

Turn the page for some exam questions on this topic ➢

EXAM QUESTION 1 ○○○

IF YOU HAVE TIME
Construct a time line showing key events in the development of quantum theory.

Before the twentieth century, physicists could not explain how stars emit electromagnetic (EM) radiation. This question is about Max Planck's contribution to a better understanding of the phenomenon.

(a) What was already known about the emission of EM radiation?

(b) What incorrect assumption had been made by physicists?

(c) How did Planck use another area of physics to correct this?

(d) Before 1900 it was suggested that the relationship between the intensity I of EM radiation and its wavelength λ was $I \propto 1/\lambda^4$, as long as the temperature remained constant. Suppose this is true, then what would happen to I as λ decreases?

(e) What actually happens to the intensity of EM radiation at low wavelengths?

(f) How did Planck explain the lower wavelength limit?

(g) How was this work extended to suggest that energy comes in small packets or quanta?

The photoelectric effect

The photoelectric effect is the ejection of electrons from a metal by a beam of sufficiently energetic (ultraviolet) radiation. The very nature of light had to be re-evaluated to explain it.

WATCH OUT
The idea that light has a dual nature (wave–particle duality) is a very difficult concept for most students.

Label this diagram.

SYLLABUS CHECK
CCEA candidates are required to know how Planck's constant can be determined experimentally. This 'stopping potential' experiment is not covered here.

Make a note of the method.

List the observations.

State the conclusions that can be drawn.

DEMONSTRATING THE PHOTOELECTRIC EFFECT   ○○○

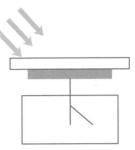

The method is very simple:

Here are the observations:

We can draw two conclusions:

Complete each of these diagrams to show what happens. W is the work function.

EXPLAINING THE PHOTOELECTRIC EFFECT   ○○○

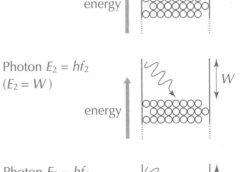

Photon $E_1 = hf_1$
$(E_1 > W)$

energy

W

Photon $E_2 = hf_2$
$(E_2 = W)$

energy

W

Photon $E_3 = hf_3$
$(E_3 < W)$

energy

W

Turn the page for some exam questions on this topic ➤

EXAM QUESTION 1 ○○○

(a) State the meaning of each term in Einstein's photoelectric equation $KE_{max} = hf - W$.

(b) Sketch a graph of KE_{max} against f.

(c) Explain how h and W can be obtained from a graph like this.

EXAM QUESTION 2 ○○○

(a) What is the photoelectric effect?

(b) Why was the wave theory of light unable to explain this effect?

(c) How did Einstein explain the photoelectric effect?

Atomic line spectra

Electrons within atoms can absorb and emit radiation. Atoms can be identified by studying the wavelengths their electrons absorb or emit. Classical physics failed to explain spectra.

SYLLABUS CHECK
Check whether your syllabus requires details of each series or just the principle of how they are formed.

This is a slightly simplified energy level diagram for a hydrogen atom. The Balmer series and the Paschen series are formed when electrons fall to energy levels $n = 2$ and $n = 3$ respectively. Complete this diagram to show these series.

Photons are emitted when electrons fall from one energy level to another. Use the diagram to show which lines in the Balmer and Paschen series produce the most energetic photons.

EMISSION SPECTRA EXPLAINED ○○○

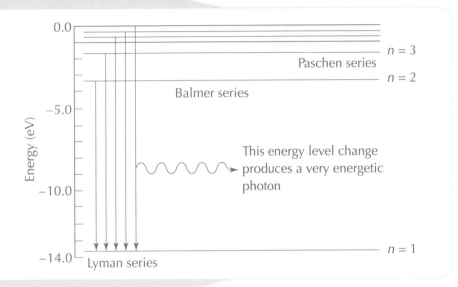

An atom can absorb a photon if it delivers exactly the right amount of energy to lift an electron from one energy level to another.

Add to this diagram to show what happens to photons (b) and (c).

ABSORPTION SPECTRA EXPLAINED ○○○

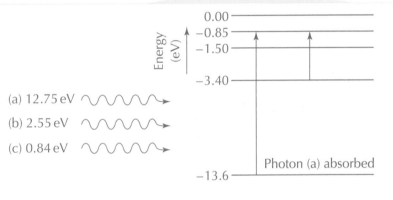

Calculate the energy of the photon emitted when an electron falls from one energy level to another as shown in the diagram. Calculate the frequency and wavelength of the emitted radiation.

PHOTON ENERGIES ○○○

The energy of the photon, emitted or absorbed, is equal to the difference between the two energy levels involved ($E = hf = E_1 - E_2$).

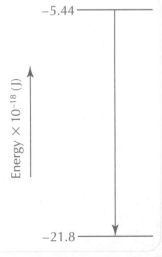

Turn the page for some exam questions on this topic ➤

EXAM QUESTION 1

(a) According to classical physics, what would happen to an electron that emitted radiation as it orbited a nucleus?

(b) Who explained the emission line spectra for hydrogen? Briefly describe their explanation.

EXAM QUESTION 2

When white light passes through a gas, the continuous spectrum is found to have a few dark lines across it.

(a) What causes these dark lines?

(b) How could the gas in question be identified?

EXAM QUESTION 3

Calculate the frequency of the spectral line caused by electrons changing from level 4 to level 2 in this energy level diagram.

DON'T FORGET
An electron-volt (eV) is a unit of energy. To convert from joules to electron-volts, divide by 1.6×10^{-19}. To convert from electron-volts to joules, multiply by 1.6×10^{-19}.

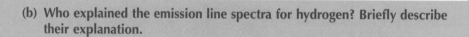

Level		Energy (eV)
4	——————	−0.85
3	——————	−1.5
2	——————	−3.4
1	——————	−6.2

EXAMINER'S SECRETS
Examiners try to construct mark schemes that reward good physics rather than penalizing poor maths. In this question you could still get two marks out of three even if you didn't convert from electron-volts into joules before using $E = hf$.

Wave–particle duality

The natural world is beautifully symmetrical. In 1924 Prince Louis de Broglie proposed that if radiation has a dual, wave–particle nature, perhaps matter has a 'split personality' too.

LINKS
For more on the photoelectric effect, see pp. 57–58.

Complete this table to show whether the phenomenon is explained by the wave theory or the quantum (particle) theory.

THE PARTICLE NATURE OF EM WAVES ○○○

In 1905 Einstein explained the photoelectric effect by assuming that light sometimes behaves as if its energy comes in packets or quanta.

Phenomenon	Explanatory theory
Diffraction	
Interference	
Polarization	
Photoelectric effect	
Line spectra	

THE WAVE NATURE OF PARTICLES ○○○

In 1924 de Broglie suggested that radiation was not unique; matter (e.g. electrons) could also have both wave and particle properties.

Complete this derivation to show how de Broglie argued that particles might have wave-like properties.

That he may sometimes have missed the target in his speculations, as for example in his theory of light quanta, cannot really be held against him.
MAX PLANCK
(REFERRING TO ALBERT EINSTEIN)

De Broglie began with the formula for the momentum of a photon:
momentum = hf/c (1)

We also have that $c = f\lambda$, which can be rearranged with λ as subject:

Taking the reciprocal gives $1/\lambda = f/c$, which allows us to rewrite (1) as

Then rearranging to make λ the subject:

De Broglie speculated that this applies to both particles and photons. Particles have momentum mv, so we can write

This is called the de Broglie wavelength.

TESTING WHETHER PARTICLES HAVE WAVE PROPERTIES ○○○

[It] seems at present to be wholly untenable.
ROBERT MILLIKAN
(WRITING OF EINSTEIN'S PHOTON THEORY)

This diagram shows an experiment similar to that used by George Thomson (son of J.J. Thomson) to prove that diffraction occurs in the foil.

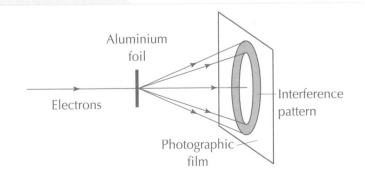

Aluminium foil

Electrons

Interference pattern

Photographic film

Say what this experiment proved.

Turn the page for some exam questions on this topic ➤

EXAM QUESTION 1 ●●●

(a) What is meant by wave–particle duality?

(b) A student suggests that when considering particles, only charged particles (e.g. electrons) exhibit a dual nature. Is this true or false?

(c) How does de Broglie's equation show the dual nature of particles?

IF YOU HAVE TIME
Examine a list of Nobel prizewinners in physics between 1901 and 1945. Pick out the discoveries or contributions you are already familiar with. This will remind you of the progress you are making in your study of physics.

EXAM QUESTION 2 ●●●

(a) Calculate the de Broglie wavelengths of (i) a car of mass 1000 kg moving at $70 \, \text{km h}^{-1}$ and (ii) an electron of mass 9.1×10^{-31} kg moving at $1.0 \times 10^7 \, \text{m s}^{-1}$.

(b) Is it easier to observe duality using a car or an electron? Explain the reason for your choice.

EXAMINER'S SECRETS
Be careful to avoid ambiguous or unclear answers. Examiners do not read ideas into a candidate's answer; they only mark what they have in front of them.

EXAM QUESTION 3 ●●●

Describe how electron diffraction gives evidence for the wave nature of particles.

Radioactivity

Radioactivity is caused by spontaneous nuclear reactions.

BACKGROUND RADIATION ○○○

Define background radiation and suggest some of its sources.

Definition

Sources

DON'T FORGET
Always use the word 'ionizing' to describe the radiation from a radioactive source.

EXAMINER'S SECRETS
Any radioactivity question based on a standard practical will test whether you know how to deal with background radiation. Always measure background radiation over a reasonably long period, then subtract it from the counts.

THE JARGON
A positron is an electron's antiparticle. It has exactly the same mass as an electron, but it is positively charged.

TYPES OF IONIZING RADIATION ○○○

Radiation	Description	Z	A
α			
β−			
β+			
γ			

Place α, β and γ in order of penetrating ability

Place α, β and γ in order of (local) ionizing ability

THE EFFECT OF DIFFERENT DECAYS ON Z, N AND A ○○○

Here N is the neutron number. But in the next section N is the number of radioactive atoms remaining. Take care to check what symbols mean.

Decay	Effect on Z	Effect on N	Effect on A
α			−4
β−	+1		
β+			
γ			

RADIOACTIVE DECAY ○○○

Define activity and give its unit.

Activity of a radioactive source is proportional to the number N of radioactive atoms remaining: $A = \lambda N$. λ is called the decay constant.
Does λ increase or decrease with increasing instability?

IF YOU HAVE TIME
Get some practice with nuclear equations. Try writing equations for the decay of a general element by each type of decay
(e.g. $_Z^A X \rightarrow _{Z-2}^{A-4} X + _2^4 \alpha$).

Decay constant λ is related to radioactive half-life ($t_{1/2}$) by the equation $\lambda t_{1/2} = 0.693$. What is radioactive half-life?

RADIOACTIVE DATING ○○○

EXAMINER'S SECRETS
Here is a common question: How could you measure a radionuclide's half-life? The link with the decay constant allows a similar question to be asked in a new way, so be prepared.

Radioactive decay can be used as a clock. What three quantities do you need to work out the age of a radioactive source?

Turn the page for some exam questions on this topic ➤

For more on this topic, see pages 44–49 of the *Revision Express A-level Study Guide*

EXAM QUESTION 1

(a) What is meant by radioactive half-life?

(b) A certain sealed-source beta emitter is known to have a half-life of a few hours. Describe how you might determine its half-life. State all safety precautions.

(c) Another radionuclide is known to have a much longer half-life. Given that a certain source contains 1.7×10^{15} atoms of this nuclide and has an activity of 4.0×10^7 Bq, calculate its decay constant and hence find its half-life.

EXAM QUESTION 2

The graph shows the *N–Z* curve for stable nuclides. Three radionuclides are found in positions A, B and C.

(a) What is the likely decay mechanism for each radionuclide? Explain your reasoning.

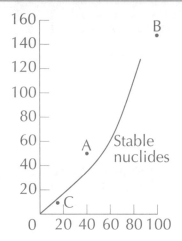

(b) A, B and C are actually $^{90}_{38}$Sr, which decays to Y, $^{238}_{92}$U, which decays to Th, and $^{22}_{11}$Na, which decays to Ne. Write balanced equations for their decay.

(c) Uranium-238 also emits gamma rays. Would you expect them to be monoenergetic (all the same energy) or not?

The nuclear atom

What *is* everything made of?

THE NUCLEAR MODEL OF THE ATOM ○○○

Label the diagram opposite to show where neutrons, protons and electrons are found.
Give the approximate diameters of the atom and the nucleus.

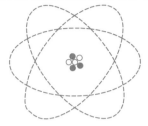

SYLLABUS CHECK
It varies from board to board how much you need to understand about other methods of probing the atom and the nucleus.

Very briefly, how was the nuclear structure of the atom discovered?

The radius of an atomic nucleus is given by $r = 1.2 \times 10^{-15} A^{1/3}$. This implies that the density of nuclear matter is constant regardless of size. Explain how.

X-ray diffraction is widely used to study atomic spacing in crystals. The Bragg equation, $n\lambda = s \sin \theta$, relates the spacing s of layers of atoms to the angular displacement θ of X-rays. Show that the X-rays must have a wavelength smaller than the atomic spacing.

Here you need to realize that the minimum number of diffraction bands is 1 and the maximum diffraction angle is 90°.

Particle diffraction can also be used to measure atoms and nuclei. A particle's wavelength depends on its energy. Explain why electrons need very high energies to probe the nucleus.

ISOTOPES AND ELEMENTS ○○○

Fill in the table.

Symbol	Name	Description
Z		
A		

WATCH OUT
A is mass number or atomic number; it is always an integer. Do not write 'atomic mass' (atomic mass isn't a whole number).

REVISION EXPRESS
For nuclear reactions, see the section on elements and isotopes in the Revision Express A-level Study Guide, pp. 42–43.

Different isotopes of an element have the same number of
but different numbers of

NUCLEAR NOTATION AND NUCLEAR REACTIONS ○○○

Any isotope of any element can be described using this notation:

nucleon number
proton number   Chemical symbol $^{A}_{Z}X$

Nuclear reactions can transmute elements: true or false?

Which quantities must be conserved in nuclear reactions?

Turn the page for some exam questions on this topic ➤

EXAM QUESTION 1 ●●●

EXAMINER'S SECRETS
This classic experiment comes up again and again in exams. Make sure you know the set-up, the reasons for using a thin gold foil, the expected results (assuming even distribution of charge and mass) and the implications of the actual results.

Rutherford, Geiger and Marsden's study of α-particle scattering by gold foil gave the first evidence for the nuclear structure of the atom.

(a) What was their evidence that most of an atom is empty space?

(b) What was their evidence that charge and mass are concentrated in a tiny nucleus?

Coulomb's law may give a clue to charge concentration, but why must mass also be concentrated?

EXAM QUESTION 2 ●●●

The approximate radius r (in metres) of an atom's nucleus is given by $r = 1.2 \times 10^{-15} A^{1/3}$. Use this equation to calculate the radius of a hydrogen nucleus ($A = 1$) and a bismuth nucleus ($A = 209$).

The mass of a nucleon is approximately 1.67×10^{-27} kg. Calculate the density of nuclear matter.

Calculate the density for hydrogen. As an extension, you could see if bismuth gives the same answer.

EXAM QUESTION 3 ●●●

This exam question is about diffraction techniques for measuring atom separations and nuclear sizes.

Radiation	λ_{min}	λ_{max}
Ultraviolet	10^{-8}	10^{-7}
X-ray	10^{-11}	10^{-7}
Gamma ray	10^{-15}	10^{-9}

LINKS
For more information on diffraction patterns, see pp. 47–48.

(a) Which radiation has suitable wavelengths for each application?

(b) Why are γ-rays unsuitable for diffraction pattern studies?

DON'T FORGET
Potential difference in volts is the energy transferred to every coulomb of charge. $1\,V = 1\,JC^{-1}$

(c) A high-energy electron's wavelength is related to its energy by $E = hc/\lambda$. Choose a suitable wavelength to probe the nucleus then calculate the required electron energy and the voltage to accelerate an electron beam to this energy. Use these values: $h = 6.63 \times 10^{-34}\,Js$, $c = 3.00 \times 10^{8}\,ms^{-1}$, $e = 1.60 \times 10^{-19}\,C$.

EXAMINER'S SECRETS
You are expected to know approximate nuclear and atomic sizes. They may not always be given in an exam question.

Nuclear energy

Nuclear energy powers the Universe!

ENERGY AND MASS   ○○○

Atoms, electrons and photons are tiny. Their masses and energies need appropriate units (SI units are too big for convenience).
The atomic mass unit (symbol u) is roughly the mass of one nucleon.

Give the proper definition of 1 u.

$1\,u = 1.661 \times 10^{-27}$ kg
The electron-volt (eV) is a unit of energy.

Define the electron-volt.

$1\,eV = 1.60 \times 10^{-19}\,C \times 1.00\,J\,C^{-1} = 1.60 \times 10^{-19}\,J$

Give the conversion from MeV to joules.

DON'T FORGET
This is particularly useful for calculating energy released by nuclear reactions. The loss in mass tells us the energy released.

According to special relativity, mass and energy are forms of the same thing (mass–energy). It turns out that $1\,u = 930$ MeV.

BINDING ENERGY   ○○○

Define binding energy.

If it costs energy to separate nucleons, sticking them together should release energy, and up to a point that's true. But beyond iron, the costs of overcoming electrostatic repulsion between protons outweigh the energy release due to binding by the strong force.

BINDING ENERGY PER NUCLEON   ○○○

Binding energy per nucleon is a measure of an atom's stability. Any nuclear reaction that increases binding energy per nucleon will release energy.

Sketch the binding energy per nucleon.

Mark the regions where fission and fusion can release energy.

Mark the position of the atoms with the maximum stability.

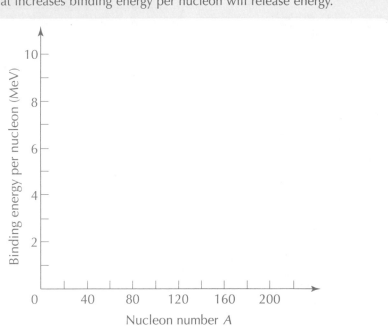

Turn the page for some exam questions on this topic ➤

Exam question 1

●●●

No need to do the graph because it's the same graph you sketched on p. 67. Part (a) is just to remind you to learn it.

SYLLABUS CHECK
Some boards do not require binding energy per nucleon at AS level, but it may come up in certain options.

EXAMINER'S SECRETS
Questions like 1(c) and (d) are favourites with examiners. They test your general understanding of physics, but within a specific context.

(a) Sketch a graph of binding energy per nucleon versus nucleon number. Then use it to explain why energy is released during nuclear fission of nuclei with high nucleons.

(b) What is it called when nuclear fission occurs naturally?

(c) Fusion of two low Z nuclei also releases energy. Why does nuclear fusion not occur naturally on Earth?

(d) Why is fusion possible in stars?

(e) Why must stars have a finite lifetime?

Exam question 2

●●●

DON'T FORGET
The differences in mass may be tiny but they are enormously important. Get used to working with highly precise data in nuclear calculations.

THE JARGON
Rest mass is the proper term for a body's mass when relativity effects can be ignored (i.e. when the body is moving far more slowly than light).

The rest mass of a proton is	1.007 276 u
The rest mass of a neutron is	1.008 665 u
The rest mass of an electron is	0.000 549 u
The rest mass of a helium-4 atom is	4.002 604 u
The rest mass of a lithium-7 atom is	7.016 005 u

The mass defect of an atom or nucleus is the difference between the mass of its constituents and its actual mass. Calculate the mass defect, binding energy and binding energy per nucleon of helium-4 and lithium-7 atoms.

Which is the more stable nuclide?

Particle physics

Don't be put off by the number of '-ons'; they do have a logic.

If I could remember the names of all these particles, I would have become a botanist

ENRICO FERMI

THE STANDARD MODEL   ○○○

Particles can be divided into hadrons and leptons. Hadrons are made of quarks. Leptons are thought to be fundamental particles. Hadrons are subdivided into baryons and mesons. Baryons are made of three quarks and mesons are made of two quarks, or more properly, a quark and an antiquark.

Name each particle (use the symbols to help you) and give their charges.

REVISION EXPRESS
For help with this, refer to the first section on nuclear and particle physics in the Revision Express A-level Study Guide; it's on pp. 144–145.

DON'T FORGET
No one has ever isolated a solitary quark.

Leptons			Charge
e^-	μ^-	τ^-	
ν_e	ν_μ	ν_τ	

Quarks			Charge
u	c	t	
d	s	b	

ANTIMATTER   ○○○

DON'T FORGET
For every particle there is an antiparticle, denoted by the same symbol but with a bar over it (the bar means 'not' or 'anti').

Every particle has an antiparticle, which is identical in all respects except that it has opposite charge. The first antiparticle to be discovered was the positron (antielectron). Given sufficient energy, particle–antiparticle pairs can be created. They can also annihilate, in which case their energy is released (e.g. as gamma radiation).

PARTICLE RECIPES   ○○○

DON'T FORGET
Except for the proton (p) and neutron (n), all symbols incorporate the particle's charge, giving a big clue to its composition.

Name the particles which have these quark combinations.

There exist too many hadrons to remember, but you must learn the make-up of the familiar baryons, the neutron (n) and the proton (p). They are made of just u and d quarks:

uud =   udd =

You may need to learn the make-up of pions (π^0, π^+, π^-); they consist of u and d quark–antiquark combinations. And perhaps also kaons (K^+, K^-), which are u and s quark–antiquark combinations.

CONSERVATION LAWS   ○○○

Name three quantities that must be conserved in any interaction.

Just give the basic conservation laws.

DON'T FORGET
Mass and energy are now considered as one thing, mass–energy.

There are several new conservation laws which are important in particle physics. Can you name three?

Give three more quantities that must be conserved in nuclear reactions.

There are others but they're not needed for AS level.

Turn the page for some exam questions on this topic ➤

EXAM QUESTION 1

● ● ●

Quark	Charge	Baryon number
u	+2/3	1/3
d	−1/3	1/3

(a) Give the composition, charge and baryon number for a proton and a neutron.

(b) Pions (pi mesons) also consist of u and d quarks and antiquarks. Give the composition, charge and baryon number for π^0, π^+ and π^-.

EXAM QUESTION 2

● ● ●

The rest mass energy of an electron is 0.511 MeV. High-energy gamma rays may annihilate by pair production (the generation of an electron–positron pair).

(a) What is the minimum energy a gamma ray must have for pair production to be possible?

(b) Given the mass–energy conversion 1 u = 930 MeV, roughly how much energy is required for proton–antiproton pairs to be created?

EXAM QUESTION 3

● ● ●

Pions are up and down quark–antiquark pairs.

(a) What type of particle is a pion?

(b) For each of these combinations, give the symbol π^+, π^- or π^0 appropriate to the particle's charge.

$u\bar{d}$

$\bar{u}d$

$\bar{u}u$

$d\bar{d}$

(c) A pion can decay into a muon. What type of particle is a muon?

(d) What quark colour change could result in decay of a π^+ into a μ^+?

(e) Which exchange boson would mediate this decay? Explain why.

Fundamental forces

According to particle theory, every interaction is mediated by exchange particles or gauge bosons. There is no such thing as action at a distance.

Fill in the table to show which forces act on which particles plus the exchange particles involved.

Draw a Feynman diagram for each interaction.

FUNDAMENTAL FORCES AND EXCHANGE PARTICLES ○○○

Every force is mediated by an exchange particle, which passes between the interacting particles. These exchanges can cause repulsion or attraction, or in the case of the weak nuclear force, changes in quark flavour plus β and ν emissions.

Force	Acts on	Exchange particle	Symbol
Gravity			
Electromagnetic			
Weak nuclear			
Strong nuclear			

W^+ is released when an up $(+2/3)$ quark changes flavour to a down $(-1/3)$ quark, e.g. in β^+ decay, where W^+ decays into a β^+ and a ν.
W^- is released when a down $(-1/3)$ quark changes to an up $(+2/3)$ quark, e.g. in β^- decay, where W^- decays into a β^- and a $\bar{\nu}$.
Z^0 takes part in interactions that do not produce any exchange of charge but they may still involve charged particles, e.g. e^-, e^+ pair production or annihilation.

FEYNMAN DIAGRAMS ○○○

These diagrams are a useful way of summarizing any interaction. Time runs up the page, so read from the base upwards. Particles are represented by arrows. The arrows do not show the direction of motion through space. Each vertex shows the emission or absorption of an exchange particle.

Electron–positron attraction

Neutron decay by β^- emission

Proton decay by electron capture

Turn the page for some exam questions on this topic ➤

EXAM QUESTION 1

● ● ●

A neutron-rich radionuclide may decay by β⁻ emission; a neutron is converted into a proton.

(a) Write an equation for this process.

(b) Which force is involved in beta decay?

(c) One type of quark has changed into another type, converting a neutron to a proton. What was the conversion?

(d) Which exchange particle is involved?

(e) Draw a Feynman diagram to represent the decay process in terms of fundamental particles (quarks, electrons and neutrinos or antineutrinos) and exchange particles.

EXAM QUESTION 2

● ● ●

Name the forces that could act between these particles.

Use the table on p. 71 to guide you; include all possible forces here.

(a) Two electrons

(b) An electron and a proton

(c) An electron and a neutron

(d) A proton and a neutron

(e) A quark and an antiquark

EXAM QUESTION 3

● ● ●

The weak interaction is mediated by high-mass virtual particles, which can only exist for tiny fractions of a second.

(a) Why are these exchange particles virtual rather than real? Why are they not normally observed outside the nucleus?

(b) Because of their large mass–energy (> 80 GeV), W and Z bosons can only exist for less than 10^{-26} second. Calculate their maximum range (if they could travel at the speed of light) and hence show why the weak interaction is normally confined to the nucleus.

Practical physics

Theories are revised or rejected in the light of experimental evidence. As a practical physicist, you have to be able to plan, carry out and assess experiments to test theories.

DON'T FORGET
Experiment is the basis of all science. Nothing is accepted without being tested. Every experiment really amounts to a test of a theory.

Summarize what each word means but don't go into great detail.

EXAMINER'S SECRETS
Remember to state the obvious. You'll be marked on what you write down. That's all an external examiner has to go on.

EXAMINATION AND COURSEWORK OPTIONS ○○○

Several boards offer both options. Both options assess the same skills. For most boards these skills are specified as follows.

Planning

Implementing

Analysing

Evaluating

PLANNING AND IMPLEMENTING ○○○

Planning

Outline the essentials of your plan.

Implementing

What steps will you take to get accurate and reliable results? How will you record them? What are examiners looking for?

SYLLABUS CHECK
Check what's being assessed, whether you're taking the examined option or the coursework option. If safety appears on your syllabus, then mention it in your assessed practical, and so on.

ANALYSING AND EVALUATING ○○○

Data should be manipulated if necessary to give a predicted straight line relationship which you can test graphically.

Give the essentials of a good graph.

Gradients and intercepts are often critical.

How do you find the gradient?

Error bars and estimates of the possible range in a gradient can be impressive. Evaluating evidence is all about identifying errors and uncertainties. After all errors have been accounted for, if the theory doesn't fit the facts then the theory may be in trouble.

73

PHYSICS

Turn the page for some exam questions on this topic ➤

EXAM QUESTION 1

● ● ●

DON'T FORGET

Good technique is essential. Mention everything you do to estimate, eliminate or minimize errors, e.g. checking micrometers for zero errors, timing oscillations from the centre where rapid motion reduces timing errors, using a fiducial mark, timing several oscillations (not just one), choosing suitably precise instruments.

The period of oscillation for a mass suspended on a spring is given by $T = 2\pi\sqrt{(m/k)}$ where T = period (s), m = mass (kg) and k = spring constant ($N\,m^{-1}$). This equation applies as long as the spring obeys Hooke's law. Plan an investigation to find out how the period of a mass suspended on a rubber band depends on its mass, i.e. to find out whether the equation holds for a rubber band. Do not measure the rubber band's spring constant directly.

Method

Fill in the empty columns. Give a suitable number of significant figures. Use the data to estimate the uncertainty in the averaged period.

Results

Mass (g)	Time for five oscillations (s)			Average T	(s)	T^2 (s^2)
50	22.0	22.4	22.6			
100	37.3	36.3	36.9			
150	49.1	50.1	48.8			
200	59.5	59.1	59.0			
250	66.0	66.3	65.7			
300	68.6	69.4	69.5			

Graph
Plot a suitable graph to test the equation.

Within experimental uncertainties, do the results support use of the equation?

Measure the gradient of your graph, hence find the band's spring constant.

DON'T FORGET

The equation of a straight line is
$y = mx + c$
where y is the y-variable on your graph, x is the x-variable, m is the gradient and c is the y-intercept.

Answer section

SEE HOW YOU GOT ON BY CHECKING AGAINST
THE ANSWERS GIVEN HERE.

Have you remembered to fill in the self-check
circles? Do this to track your progress.

For more detail on the topics covered in this book,
you can check the *Revision Express A-level Study
Guide,* your class notes or your own textbook.
You can also find exam questions and model
answers at www.revision-express.com.

Don't forget, tear out these answers and put
them in your folder for handy revision reference!

Scalars and vectors

If direction matters, you are dealing with a *vector* quantity. New rules of addition and subtraction apply. Can you apply them?

VECTOR QUANTITIES

Some vector quantities are displacement, velocity, acceleration, force, weight, momentum.

> List as many vector quantities as you can in the space provided.

VECTOR ADDITION AND SUBTRACTION

Vectors can be added using scale drawings. If two forces F_1 and F_2 act at an angle θ, their resultant can be found by the **parallelogram rule**.

$$R = F_1 + F_2$$

> Draw a diagram to illustrate the parallelogram rule.

Now sketch the parallelogram you would use to subtract F_2 from F_1.

$$R' = F_1 - F_2$$

Vector subtraction

Reverse its direction and then add it.

> State the rule for subtracting one vector from another.

RESOLVING VECTORS INTO PERPENDICULAR COMPONENTS

Any vector can be resolved into perpendicular component vectors. This allows us to consider horizontal and vertical motion separately, or to distinguish between forces acting along a plane and normal (at 90°) to a plane.

Why do we usually resolve velocity into horizontal and vertical components?

Because gravity affects only vertical motion.

> Show how you would resolve an arrow's velocity v into a horizontal component v_x and a vertical component v_y.

Turn the page for some exam questions on this topic ▶

For more on this topic, see pages 4–5 of the *Revision Express A-level Study Guide*

EXAM QUESTION 1

Two forces act simultaneously on a body. The size of the resultant force is 160 N. One of the forces is 100 N in magnitude.

(a) Which of the following forces could be the second force?

50 N [ ]   250 N [✓]   150 N [✓]   300 N [ ]

(b) If the size of the second force is 120 N, use a scale drawing or another method to find the angle between the two forces.

120 N   160 N   87°   100 N

> Put a tick next to each force which could give a resultant of 160 N when added to a 100 N force.

> Use a scale drawing to find the angle. You will need to use a pair of compasses. Use the space opposite to show how you did it.

EXAM QUESTION 2

An aeroplane flies horizontally at a steady velocity of 100 m s⁻¹. It drops a small, heavy parcel. Assuming air resistance is negligible, find the parcel's speed 5.0 s later. Take $g = 9.81$ m s⁻².

After 5.0 s
$v_y = 0 + 9.81 \times 5.0$
$= 49 \text{ m s}^{-1}$
$v = \sqrt{(100^2 + 49^2)}$
$= 110 \text{ m s}^{-1}$ (2 s.f.)

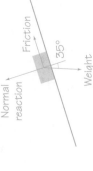

100 m s⁻¹   49 m s⁻¹   v

> Draw a sketch to help you.

EXAM QUESTION 3

A block rests on a rough board which is tilted at a gradient of 35°.

(a) Draw a free-body force diagram for the block.

Normal reaction   Friction   35°   Weight

(b) If the block weighs 40 N, calculate the size of the frictional force preventing the block from sliding down the board.

Friction $= 40 \sin 35° = 23$ N (to 2 s.f.)

(c) The board is thin and fragile. If the normal force acting on its surface exceeds 35 N, it will break. The board is slowly lowered towards the horizontal.

(i) Will it break?

Yes

(ii) If so, at what angle?

When $40 \cos \theta = 35$ N, i.e. when $\theta = 29°$

LINKS
To find out more about free-body force diagrams, see pp. 17–18.

© Pearson Education Limited 2001

Forces and moments in equilibrium

AS AQA:A AQA:B CCEA EDEXCEL OCR:A OCR:B WJEC

This section is essentially about static objects. For any object to remain at rest, the forces and moments acting on and about each and every point must be balanced.

DON'T FORGET
You can add vectors together by drawing a sequence of arrows, tail to nose. If a body is in equilibrium, the nose of the last force arrow will touch the tail of the first, making a closed polygon.

To check that the forces on the pulley are balanced, rearrange the force arrows to form a triangle.

FORCE POLYGONS
Free-body force diagrams show all the forces acting on a body. If the body is static, the sum of the forces must equal zero, so the force vectors will add up (tail to nose) to form a closed polygon.

○○○

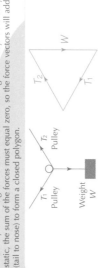

MOMENTS
The moment of a force about a point is given by

$$moment = Fd$$

where F is the magnitude of the force and d is the perpendicular distance from the line of action of the force to the point.

Write an equation and define terms.

In the diagram below, the moment about point P is 30 N m. Find the size of the force F.

$$d = 2.00\ cos\ 30° = 1.73\ m; \quad F = 30/1.73 = 17.3\ N$$

○○○

THE PRINCIPLE OF MOMENTS
If a body is in rotational equilibrium,

Complete the sentence to state the principle of moments in your own words.

the sum of the clockwise moments is equal and opposite to the sum of the anticlockwise moments (about every point in the body).

STATICS PROBLEMS: TWO COMMON TYPES
* Problems involving three (or occasionally more) forces, acting at different angles on the same body (effectively on the same point). To solve these problems, you can use

Complete the sentence.

the triangle (or polygon) of forces

* Problems involving beams and rigid bodies, with forces acting at different points. To solve these, you need to use

Complete the sentence.

the principle of moments

○○○

Turn the page for some exam questions on this topic ►

For more on this topic, see pages 6–7 of the *Revision Express A-level Study Guide*

EXAM QUESTION 1

An archer draws a bow by pulling on the bowstring with a horizontal force of 200 N, keeping the bowstring's tension above the arrow equal to the bowstring's tension below the arrow. Given the angles shown in the diagram, find this tension by scale drawing.

$T = 200N$

200N

T $60°$ T
$30°$ $60°$ $60°$ $30°$
200N

○○○

LINKS
For more information on free-body force diagrams, see pp. 17–18.

Draw a triangle of forces and find T, the tension in the bow.

EXAM QUESTION 2

A cable-car is suspended on a cable between pylons A and B.

T_B
a
T_A
A
B

○○○

EXAMINER'S SECRETS
Although the triangle of forces can be used to solve problems like this, it is often easier to resolve forces into horizontal and vertical components, then use the fact that the forces balance in each direction.

(a) If T_A is the tension in the cable on the side towards A and T_B is the tension on the side towards B, describe qualitatively the changes in T_A and T_B as the car makes its way from A to B. Explain your answer.

$T_A\ cos\ a = T_B\ cos\ b.$ Close to A, angle $a >$ angle $b, \Rightarrow cos\ a < cos\ b \Rightarrow T_A > T_B.$ As the car approaches B, T_A decreases and T_B increases. $T_A = T_B$ at the centre. Closer to B, $T_B > T_A.$

(b) If the cable-car weighs 5000 N and the distance between A and B is 200 m and the cable is 220 m long, calculate the maximum tension the cable must be capable of holding (assume the cable does not stretch and is very light).

6000 N (when the car is at the centre)

At A and B, the car hangs down as low as it possibly can and either A or B carries the whole 5000 N. As it travels towards the centre, the car has to be lifted and this requires extra tension.

Considering only the horizontal components of the tension forces, find an equation linking T_A and T_B then use it to answer the question.

EXAM QUESTION 3

A painter stands on a rigid board supported by two trestles. The painter weighs 500 N and the board weighs 100 N. Given the dimensions shown, calculate the weight held by each trestle.

0.50 m 0.50 m 1.00 m

500 N 100 N

Write down the sequence of steps you followed to get the answer.

1. Total weight held = 600 N
2. Apply principle of moments (about a support)

425 N (l)

175 N (r)

○○○

For more on this topic, see pages 8–9 of the *Revision Express A-level Study Guide*

EXAM QUESTION 1

A beanbag is thrown up vertically in the air. When it lands, it does not bounce. Assume air resistance is negligible.

(a) Sketch a graph of its height above the ground against time.

(b) Sketch a graph of its velocity against time, taking upwards as the positive direction.

(c) Explain how you would determine the magnitude of the gravitational acceleration g from the velocity–time graph.

g = the gradient

(d) If the effects of air resistance were significant, the velocity–time graph would change. Which region of the graph would then give the best estimate of g? Explain your answer.

The region where the bag's velocity is closest to zero. Air resistance decreases at lower speeds.

© Pearson Education Limited 2001

EXAMINER'S SECRETS

This question comes up in various forms with reassuring regularity. You may be given an initial velocity (in which case your sketch should include velocity values). You may be asked how to determine the height gained from the velocity–time graph.

IF YOU HAVE TIME

Try sketching the velocity–time graph of an object thrown up in the air, assume that air resistance *is* significant.

REVISION EXPRESS

Air resistance is proportional to v^2. Find out more about drag and lift on pp. 20–21 of the Revision Express A-level Study Guide.

EXAM QUESTION 2

The graph shows how a skydiver's downward velocity varied with time during a particular fall.

(a) When did the skydiver's parachute open?

After exactly 15 s

(b) Describe and explain the motion shown in every 5 s interval.

0–5   Steady acceleration (at $9.8\ m\ s^{-2}$)
5–10   Acceleration drops to zero as the skydiver speeds up
10–15 Steady (terminal) velocity $-70\ m\ s^{-1}$
15–20 Sudden deceleration as parachute opens
       Rate drops to zero as parachutist slows
20–25 Steady (terminal) velocity $-10\ m\ s^{-1}$

(c) From what height did the skydiver fall? Show how you found it.

Area under graph = 1100 m

Use the graph to answer each part of the question. Show your methods.

IF YOU HAVE TIME

Explain the skydive in terms of the forces acting.

EXAMINER'S SECRETS

Problems involving uniform acceleration are easier to solve using the equations of motion. Problems with varying acceleration rates will be used to check your understanding of graphs of motion.

Ways of describing motion

The most concise way to describe motion is to use a graph.

DEFINITIONS

Quantity	Symbol	Definition	SI unit
Displacement	s	distance in a certain direction	m
Velocity	v	speed in a certain direction	$m\ s^{-1}$
Acceleration	a	rate of increase in velocity	$m\ s^{-2}$

Define each term. Give its symbol and its SI unit.

DISTANCE–TIME GRAPHS AND DISPLACEMENT–TIME GRAPHS

In any journey, the distance travelled can only increase, so the gradient of a distance–time graph is always *positive*. Instantaneous speed is equal to the *gradient of a distance-time graph.*

Fill in the gaps.

C shows acceleration
B shows constant speed
A shows deceleration

Match the letter to the statement.

What is the average speed of each object over the 10 km journey?

Average speed = (distance travelled)/(time taken)
= 5 km h^{-1}

Write the formula for average speed, then work out the answers.

When the direction of travel matters, it makes more sense to use a displacement–time graph. Its gradient tells us an object's *velocity*. Sketch a displacement–time graph for a bouncing ball.

Start at maximum height (so the ball has a reason to fall).

VELOCITY–TIME GRAPHS

You can use a velocity–time graph to find a body's displacement and its acceleration at any instant (as well as its velocity).

Displacement

Displacement = area under a velocity–time graph

Acceleration

Acceleration = gradient of a velocity–time graph

Describe how you would determine each quantity from a velocity–time graph.

Turn the page for some exam questions on this topic ▶

Equations of motion

The equations of motion are essential for solving problems involving constant acceleration.

SYMBOLS AND THEIR DEFINITIONS

Name and define each term. Give its SI unit and give a tick to each vector quantity.

Symbol	Definition	Unit	Tick if vector
s	displacement (distance in a given direction)	m	✓
u	initial velocity (initial rate of increase in displacement)	m s^{-1}	✓
v	final velocity (after body has accelerated for time t)	m s^{-1}	✓
a	acceleration (rate of increase in velocity)	m s^{-2}	✓
t	time taken for the change in velocity	s	

EXAMINER'S SECRETS

Your first step in solving any problem involving equations of motion should be to write down these five quantities and any values you're given. This helps to crystallize the problem in your mind.

EQUATIONS OF MOTION

Complete the three standard equations of motion:

$$v = u + at \qquad (1)$$
$$s = ut + \tfrac{1}{2}at^2 \qquad (2)$$
$$v^2 = u^2 + 2as \qquad (3)$$

Show how the equation for velocity derives from the definition of acceleration.

$$a = (\text{increase in velocity})/t = (v - u)/t, \text{ so } v = u + at$$

Write an equation for displacement in terms of average velocity and time, then in terms of symbols u, v and t.

$$\text{displacement} = \text{average velocity} \times \text{time}$$
$$s = \tfrac{1}{2}(u + v)t = \tfrac{1}{2}ut + \tfrac{1}{2}vt$$

Replace v by ($u + at$) and hence derive equation (2).

$$s = \tfrac{1}{2}ut + \tfrac{1}{2}vt = \tfrac{1}{2}ut + \tfrac{1}{2}(u + at)t = ut + \tfrac{1}{2}at^2$$

EXAMINER'S SECRETS

Manipulating equations gets easier the more often you do it. Be careful and don't rush. Get into good habits from the start. Give a separate line to every operation you perform on an equation.

CHANGING THE SUBJECT

What rules must be followed when you want to make a different term the subject of an equation?

Whatever you do to one side of the equation, you must also do to the other. Brackets can help, e.g.

$$v^2 = u^2 + 2as \Rightarrow v^2 - u^2 = 2as \Rightarrow a = (v^2 - u^2)/2s$$

Turn the page for some exam questions on this topic ➤

For more on this topic, see pages 10–11 of the *Revision Express A-level Study Guide*

EXAM QUESTION 1

In a relay race, runner A has to pass the baton to runner B, who waits at the start of a 5.00 m changeover box. B can start running at any time, but A must successfully pass B the baton at some point within the box. A approaches B at a steady speed of 9.00 m s^{-1}.

To answer this question, first write down what limits B's top speed within the box.

(a) **If B can accelerate from rest at 5.50 m s^{-2}, when (i.e. how many seconds before the handover) should B set off?**

B should be running as fast as possible at the changeover but must not be going faster than A.
Data: $s = 5.00$ m, $a = 5.50$ m s^{-2}, $u = 0$
$s = ut + \tfrac{1}{2}at^2 \Rightarrow t^2 = 2 \times 5.00/5.50$ so $t = 1.35$ s
Check B's top speed is less than A's. We have
$v = u + at = 5.50 \times 1.35 = 7.43$ m s^{-1}, therefore A will catch B.

(b) **Use your answer to calculate how far away A is from B when B starts running.**

In 1.35 s, A will run $1.35 \times 9.00 = 12.15$ m. This includes the changeover box (5.00 m), so A is 7.15 m away when B starts running.

IF YOU HAVE TIME

Try assuming B can accelerate faster, e.g. at 6.50 m s^{-2}, at least for a short time. Can you still work out when B should set off?

EXAM QUESTION 2

A bungee jumper falls freely from rest for 15.0 m before the bungee begins to stretch.

(a) **Calculate their speed when the bungee just starts to stretch.**

Data: $u = 0$, $s = 15.0$ m, $a = 9.81$ m s^{-2}
$v^2 = u^2 + 2as = 294$ m^2 s^{-2}, so $v = 17.2$ m s^{-1}

(b) **Is this the jumper's top speed? Justify your answer.**

No. The upward force gradually increases as the bungee is stretched. Top speed is not reached until the upward force equals the jumper's weight.

(c) **If the bungee brings the jumper to a halt in a further 5 m, calculate the jumper's average acceleration in this last 5 m.**

$s = 5$ m, $u = 17.2$ m s^{-1}, $v = 0$
$v^2 = u^2 + 2as$, so $a = -29.6$ m s^{-2}

IF YOU HAVE TIME

Sketch a free-body force diagram for the bungee jumper (a) in free fall (b) when they have reached their top speed and (c) when the bungee is at maximum extension. Say which force is biggest in each case.

EXAM QUESTION 3

A diver jumps from a springboard at a speed of 6.5 m s^{-1} and at an angle of 60° above the horizontal. The springboard is 0.60 m above the surface of the water.

(a) **Calculate the maximum height reached above the water's surface.**

Initial upward velocity $u_y = 6.5 \sin 60° = 5.6$ m s^{-1}.
Use $v^2 = u^2 + 2as$. Taking upwards as the positive direction,
$a = -9.8$ m s^{-2} ($-g$ to 2 s.f.), $v = 0$, so $s = 1.6$ m.
Maximum height above water = 2.2 m.

(b) **Calculate the diver's speed as they hit the water.**

$v^2 = u^2 + 2as$ gives $v = \sqrt{(2 \times 9.8 \times 2.2)} = 6.6$ m s^{-1}

Projectiles

Projectiles are subject to gravity. Projectile problems require you to consider vertical and horizontal motion separately.

GRAVITATIONAL ACCELERATION

Projectile problems set at AS level will normally include the assumption that air resistance is negligible. This allows us to treat vertical acceleration as constant (g) and to assume horizontal speed does not change.

Two balls roll off a table at different speeds. How would you calculate the horizontal distance each ball travels before hitting the ground?

> *Assume you have all the information you need to solve the problem, i.e. the table's height and the initial speed of each ball.*

1. To calculate the time taken to hit the ground, use
$s_y = u_y t + \frac{1}{2} a_y t^2$. Since $u_y = 0$ and $a_y = g$, $t = \sqrt{(2s_y/g)}$.

2. Use this time in $s_x = v_x t$ to calculate each ball's range. Horizontal velocity does not vary as the ball falls.

RESOLVING HORIZONTAL AND VERTICAL MOTION

A projectile has a velocity v, magnitude v, directed at an angle θ above the horizontal; write the magnitudes of the horizontal and vertical components (v_x and v_y) in terms of v and θ.

> **SPEED LEARNING**
> Definitions of sine, cosine and tangent are summarized by **SohCahToa**.
> Sine: opposite over hypotenuse.
> Cosine: adjacent over hypotenuse.
> Tangent: opposite over adjacent.

$v_x = v \cos \theta$
$v_y = v \sin \theta$

MAXIMUM HEIGHT, FLIGHT TIME AND RANGE

> *State which quantities are needed for each calculation.*

(a) What information do you need for calculating maximum height?

Initial vertical velocity u_y, the fact that vertical velocity is zero at the top of the flight, gravitational acceleration g, and initial height.

(b) What information do you need for calculating flight time?

The same information as in (a).

What information do you need for calculating range?

Flight time t and horizontal velocity v_x.

> *Take one step at a time. Write down the quantities you know. Calculate the maximum height reached. Work out the time for the flight. Work out the ball's range.*

Calculate the maximum height and range of a golf ball hit at a speed of 45.0 m s⁻¹ at 40.0° above the horizontal. Assume no air resistance.

We know $u_x = 45.0 \cos 40.0° = 34.5$ m s⁻¹
$u_y = 45.0 \sin 40.0° = 28.9$ m s⁻¹

If upward velocity is positive then $g = -9.81$ m s⁻².
For max. height, use $v^2 = u^2 + 2as$.
Velocity at max. height is 0, so
$0 = 28.9^2 + (2 \times -9.81 \times s_x)$ max. height $s_x =$ **42.6 m**
For half of the flight, using $v = u + at$ (vertically).
$0 = 28.9 - 9.81t$, so $t = 2.95$ s
Time for entire flight = 5.90 s   range = 34.5×5.90
= **204 m**

Turn the page for some exam questions on this topic ➤

For more on this topic, see pages 12–13 of the *Revision Express A-level Study Guide*

EXAM QUESTION 1

Balls A and B are thrown off a cliff at the same speed. A is thrown at angle θ above the horizontal, B at angle θ below the horizontal. Which hits the ground with the greatest speed? Explain your answer.

> *Sketch the trajectory of each ball, then answer the question in the space opposite.*

They hit the ground at the same speed. If air resistance is negligible, the speed of a projectile on the rise is exactly the same as its speed on the fall, at the same height above ground. This is because energy is conserved. On the way down, both balls have the same velocity at cliff-top level and both are subject to the same acceleration, so they hit the ground at the same speed.

EXAM QUESTION 2

(a) A long-jumper takes off at an angle of 25° above the horizontal. If their take-off speed is 10.5 m s⁻¹, how long will their jump be?

> *Sketch the jumper's initial trajectory, resolve their speed into horizontal and vertical components and solve the problem.*

Horizontal velocity $v_x = 10.5 \cos 25° = 9.52$ m s⁻¹
Initial vert. velocity $u_y = 10.5 \sin 25° = 4.44$ m s⁻¹
Time to max. height = time for vertical velocity to fall to zero

Using $v_y = u_y + at$, we have $0 = 4.44 - 9.81t$,
so $t = 0.45$ s for half the jump. Time taken for entire jump = 0.90 s. Range = $9.52 \times 0.90 =$ **8.57 m**

(b) What would be the jumper's range if they could achieve a 45° take-off with the same launch speed?

$v_x = 10.5 \cos 45° = 7.42$ m s⁻¹
$v_y = 10.5 \sin 45° = 7.42$ m s⁻¹
Time for entire jump = $2 \times 7.42/9.81 = 1.51$ s
Range = $7.42 \times 1.51 =$ **11.2 m**

Newton's laws of motion

When it comes to mechanics, Newton's laws are the absolute essentials.

NEWTON'S FIRST LAW OF MOTION

Write Newton's first law of motion in your own words.

A body will remain at rest, or will keep moving with constant speed in a straight line unless acted upon by unbalanced external forces.

What is inertia?

Inertia is a disinclination to accelerate under action of an unbalanced force. Mass is a measure of inertia (mass is inertia).

DON'T FORGET
Balanced forces imply constant velocity, and constant velocity implies balanced forces.

A cyclist exerts a forward force of 300 N and travels at a constant speed along a straight road. What can you say about the forces resisting the cyclist's motion?

They add up to 300 N and they act in the opposite direction.

If the cyclist increases the forwards force to 400 N, what will happen?

The cyclist will accelerate. As they speed up, drag forces will rise and a new equilibrium will soon be set up, at a higher speed.

NEWTON'S SECOND LAW OF MOTION

This law describes the effect of an unbalanced force on a body's motion. Write it as an equation relating force, mass and acceleration.

$$Force = mass \times acceleration$$

$$F = ma$$

DON'T FORGET
Acceleration is the clue that tells you forces are unbalanced.

What can you say about the directions of force and acceleration?

Force and acceleration are always in exactly the same direction.

If the cyclist's mass is 50 kg, what is their initial acceleration when they raise the forward force from 300 N to 400 N?

Net forward force = 100 N, so $a = 2$ m s^{-2}

NEWTON'S THIRD LAW OF MOTION

Write Newton's third law of motion here.

If body A exerts a force on body B, then body B exerts an equal and opposite force on body A. In other words, for every action there is an equal and opposite reaction.

WATCH OUT
Action and reaction are always the same sort of force (both are contact forces, both are gravitational forces, etc.) and they act on different bodies.

Why can action and reaction forces never balance each other?

Because they always act on different bodies.

Give some examples of action and reaction pairs.

Earth pulls Moon   Moon pulls Earth

Turn the page for some exam questions on this topic ➤

For more on this topic, see pages 14–15 of the *Revision Express A-level Study Guide*

EXAM QUESTION 1

(a) State in words Newton's second law of motion.

The acceleration of a body is directly proportional to, and in the same direction as, the resultant force acting.

Acceleration is inversely proportional to the body's mass.

Alternative: A body's rate of change of momentum is directly proportional to the net force acting on it.

You can use these words in your definition: force, mass, acceleration. But avoid the word 'equals' since $F = ma$ only works with carefully chosen units.

(b) Explain how the newton is defined.

1 newton is the resultant force required to accelerate a 1 kg mass at a rate of 1 m s^{-2}.

(c) Describe, with the aid of diagrams, an experiment you could carry out to verify Newton's second law.

Trolley   Variable mass

Pulley

Ticker   Ticker   Friction-compensated   Weight = net force
tape   timer   ramp

1. Keeping the trolley mass constant, vary the net force. Measure the corresponding acceleration, $(v - u)/t$, using a ticker timer or light gates. Plot a against F. Straight line through origin shows $a \propto F$.

2. Keeping the net force constant, vary the trolley's mass. Measure acceleration as before and plot a graph of a against $1/m$. Straight line through the origin shows $a \propto 1/m$ (i.e. acceleration is inversely proportional to mass).

EXAMINER'S SECRETS
This question tests your understanding of a standard practical. Can you describe clearly what you did and why you did it? Remember that Newton's second law is all about acceleration. What does a depend on? Would you plot any graphs? Why?

EXAM QUESTION 2

(a) A certain car can apply a maximum braking force of 2500 N.
Calculate its braking distance when travelling at 20 m s^{-1} if the combined mass of the car and its driver is 500 kg.

$a = 2500/500 = 5.0$ m s^{-2}. Now use $v^2 = u^2 + 2as$.

If forwards is positive, a is negative

$\Rightarrow 0 = 20^2 - 2 \times 5 \times s$ $s = 40$ m

This question is about braking distance and total stopping distance. Before plugging in numbers, make a note of the factors affecting each one.

(b) Fully loaded with passengers and luggage, the car is 50% heavier. What is its loaded braking distance?

$a = 2500/750 = 3.3$ m s^{-2}

$s = 400/(2 \times 3.3) = 60$ m (i.e. 50% greater)

Make a guess, then calculate the answer.

(c) Total stopping distance will normally be greater than this. Why?

Total stopping distance = thinking distance (distance travelled between stop stimulus and braking response) + braking distance. Also, the force quoted is a maximum. There has to be a build-up period during which $F < F_{max}$.

LINKS
Another approach to stopping distances is to consider the work necessary to reduce a body's kinetic energy ($\frac{1}{2}mv^2$) to zero. For more on this approach, see pp. 21–22.

Free-body force diagrams

A free-body force diagram should be your starting point in virtually every mechanics problem.

FORCES AND THEIR DIRECTIONS

The most common forces in AS level problems are weight, thrust or driving force, friction, drag, lift and the normal reaction. For each of these forces, state the direction.

Fill in the directions.

Force	Direction
Weight	downwards
Driving force	forwards
Friction, drag	opposing relative motion
Lift	upwards, at 90° to the wings
Normal reaction	upwards, at 90° to the surface

REVISION EXPRESS

To calculate the normal reaction, you first have to work out the action (i.e. the contact force of the body on the surface). This is often, but not always, equal in size to the component of the body's weight acting at 90° into the surface. See pp. 16–17 of the Revision Express A-level Study Guide.

FREE-BODY FORCE DIAGRAMS

A free-body force diagram shows the forces acting on a particular body and nothing else. Draw free-body force diagrams for (a) a block resting on a rough inclined surface; (b) a caravan being towed at a steady speed up a slope; and (c) an aeroplane flying horizontally at a steady speed, banking its wings at an angle of 25° to turn.

(a)

(b)

(c)

Set out the force balance along the surface and normal to the surface.

Block

Force balance along surface
    Friction $F = W \sin \theta$ (W = weight of block)
Force balance normal to surface
    Normal reaction $N = W \cos \theta$

Constant velocity implies balanced forces. Set out the force balance along the slope and normal to the slope.

Caravan

Force balance along slope
    Towbar tension $T = mg \sin \theta$ + friction + drag
Force balance normal to slope
    Normal reaction $N = mg \cos \theta$

Say whether the forces balance vertically and whether they balance horizontally. Write expressions for any force balances or resultant forces.

Aeroplane

Force balance vertically
    $L \cos 25° = W$ (L = lift, W = weight)
Forces do not balance horizontally; there is a resultant sideways force of magnitude $L \sin 25°$

Turn the page for some exam questions on this topic ▶

For more on this topic, see pages 14–17 of the *Revision Express A-level Study Guide*

EXAM QUESTION 1

A car of mass 750 kg is driven up a 15° hill at a constant velocity. If the car's engines provide a driving force of 5000 N, calculate the size of the combined drag and friction forces acting on the car.

Draw a free-body force diagram. Calculate the car's weight (assume g = 9.81 m s⁻²), then solve the problem.

Weight $W = 750 \times 9.81$
            $= 7400$ N
Constant velocity
    $\Rightarrow$ forces are balanced
Along road
    drag + friction + $W \sin 15°$
                            $= 5000$ N
So drag + friction = **3100 N**

EXAM QUESTION 2

A lift in a skyscraper contains a set of bathroom scales. Passengers can stand on the scales to see what the ride does to their 'weight' (strictly, what it does to the contact force). The lift has a fixed maximum speed, which it reaches quite rapidly.

(a) Describe qualitatively what happens to the reading on the scales as the passenger ascends from the ground floor to the top floor.

There is not enough space here to sketch force diagrams, but you should do them somewhere.

The scales show the contact force. If W is the passenger's weight and F the contact force, then during the initial acceleration $F > W$. When the lift reaches its top speed $F = W$. When the lift slows its ascent $F < W$. When the lift has stopped $F = W$.

(b) The passenger's mass is 65 kg. What is happening to them when the scales read 40 kg? Be as quantitative as you can.

The forces acting on the passenger are W, weight (downwards) and F, the contact force from the scales (upwards). $W = 65$ kg = 640 N. $F = 40$ kg = 390 N. The net force = 250 N, so the passenger is accelerating downwards at 250/65 = 3.8 m s⁻².

EXAM QUESTION 3

A mechanic uses a block and tackle to lift a car's engine out of a car. If all pulleys are friction-free and 800 N is the tension in the rope while the engine is held steady, what is the weight of the engine?

Solve this problem by resolving forces horizontally and vertically. The tension in the rope is the same everywhere.

The vector sum of all the forces is zero. W acts straight down in the force triangle and is given by
$W = \sqrt{(1600^2 - 800^2)}$
    = **1400 N** (2 s.f.)

Momentum and impulse

Momentum is the tendency to keep moving steadily. Impulse is the only thing that can alter a body's momentum.

THE LAW OF CONSERVATION OF MOMENTUM

The total momentum of any isolated system before any interaction is exactly the same as the total momentum after it. Momentum is conserved in every interaction.

Define momentum in words and symbols.

Word	momentum	equals	mass times velocity
Symbol	p	$=$	mv

When two objects collide, the momentum gained by one equals the momentum lost by the other. For a collision between two bodies, the law of conservation of momentum can be summarized as follows:

Total amount of momentum before collision is equal to total amount of momentum after collision:

$$(m_1v_1 + m_2v_2) = (m_1v_1 + m_2v_2)$$
$$\text{before} \qquad\qquad \text{after}$$

State the law of conservation of momentum in your own words. Translate your law into a useful equation. Define all terms.

where m = mass, v = velocity (in chosen direction) and the subscripts 1 and 2 refer to the two bodies.

DON'T FORGET
Momentum is a vector quantity. Choose which direction is positive before you start doing calculations.

Why is momentum conservation often difficult to demonstrate in collisions between trolleys or cars?

Because the trolleys or cars are not completely isolated from the rest of the world. Some momentum is transferred to the world.

IMPULSE

○○○

Define impulse and say what it causes.

Impulse is the product of resultant force and time. Impulse causes a change in momentum.

Write the equation linking impulse and momentum.

$$Ft = mv - mu \quad (\text{impulse} = \text{change in momentum})$$

DON'T FORGET
The units of impulse are the same as the units of momentum.
$1\ \text{N s} = 1\ \text{kg m s}^{-1}$.
You must be familiar with both units.

This is a more general version of Newton's second law of motion. It simplifies to $F = ma$ when m and a are constant.
Find the impulse to accelerate a 90 kg go-kart from $10\ \text{m s}^{-1}$ to $12\ \text{m s}^{-1}$.

$$\text{Impulse} = 90 \times (12 - 10) = 180\ \text{N s}$$

EXAMINER'S SECRETS
The impulse equation provides a way of solving problems involving rockets and jets (the force produced by a constant stream of matter, etc.). These problems regularly crop up in various guises.

A fire hose exerts a force of 80 N on a fire-fighter when a jet of water is pumped out at $20\ \text{m s}^{-1}$. Calculate flow rate of the water in the jet.

Flow rate is the mass of water per second (m/t):

$$m/t = F/(v - u) = 80/20 = 4\ \text{kg s}^{-1}$$

Turn the page for some exam questions on this topic ▶

For more on this topic, see pages 24–25 of the *Revision Express A-level Study Guide*

EXAM QUESTION 1

○○○

A train couples up to a stationary truck by shunting into it. The train's mass is 220 tonnes and the truck's mass is 60 tonnes. The train runs into the truck at $0.75\ \text{m s}^{-1}$. Calculate the combined speed of the train and truck after the collision (neglecting friction).

Before collision: $p = 220 \times 0.75 + 60 \times 0$
$= 165\ \text{t m s}^{-1}$

After collision: $p = 280v\ \text{t m s}^{-1}$ so $v = 0.59\ \text{m s}^{-1}$

EXAM QUESTION 2

○○○

A rocket fires out hot exhaust gases at rate $400\ \text{kg s}^{-1}$ and at speed $10\ \text{km s}^{-1}$ (relative to the rocket). Find the net force on the rocket.

$F = (v - u)m/t = 10^4\ \text{m s}^{-1} \times 400\ \text{kg s}^{-1} = 4 \times 10^6\ \text{N}$

What will happen to the rocket's rate of acceleration over the next few seconds? Assume the engine's performance remains constant.

Constant force and decreasing mass
$\Rightarrow$ increasing acceleration

EXAMINER'S SECRETS
Learn this version of the impulse equation. It comes up very often in jet problems.

EXAM QUESTION 3

○○○

An asteroid is heading towards Earth. Its mass is 1.5×10^{13} kg and its velocity is $25\ \text{km s}^{-1}$, directly towards the centre of the Earth.

Calculate the asteroid's momentum.

$p = mv = 3.8 \times 10^{17}\ \text{kg m s}^{-1}$

Scientists come up with two plans of action. Plan A involves sending a rocket to knock the asteroid off its path. The rocket's maximum mass and speed (on impact) are 2.0×10^4 kg and $1.0 \times 10^7\ \text{m s}^{-1}$.

If the rocket hits the asteroid inelastically when it is 1.5×10^8 m away from the Earth's centre, could the plan work? The Earth's radius is about 6.5×10^6 m.

DON'T FORGET
Inelastic collisions are where the two colliding objects join together. All momentum is shared by the combined body.

The impact gives the asteroid a sideways momentum of $2.0 \times 10^{11}\ \text{kg m s}^{-1}$ and a velocity of $1.3 \times 10^{-2}\ \text{m s}^{-1}$.

First decide the direction from which the rocket should hit the asteroid. Calculate the sideways momentum and velocity imparted by the collision. Use the asteroid's speed to calculate the time to expected impact. Will the asteroid hit or miss?

The time to arrive at the centre of the Earth is 6000 s. The sideways movement in this time is 78 m. Plan A won't work.

Plan B is to send a team of experts to land on the asteroid, drill into it, plant a bomb and explode the asteroid into a thousand pieces. What effect will this have on the path of the asteroid's centre of mass?

None

You have to assume that the full impact would cause worldwide devastation to answer this question.

What effect will it have on the likely Earth impact? Consider best and worst cases.

At best, most of the fragments are scattered and miss the Earth completely. At worst, all fragments still hit the Earth. Each impact will be smaller and atmospheric burn-up will reduce impacts further.

Which plan wins?

Plan B wins; it has a chance of some success.

© Pearson Education Limited 2001

Work, energy and power

Energy transfer drives every process.

WORK

Work is the transfer of energy. Work is done whenever a force moves an object. Work done is defined by the equation:

$$\text{work done} = \text{force} \times \text{distance moved in the force's direction}$$
$$\text{(J)} \qquad \text{(N)} \qquad \text{(m)}$$

$$\text{Work done} = F \cos\theta\, s$$

> Write the defining equation in the space provided. Give units.

> Now write the formula for a force acting at an angle θ to the object's direction of motion.

WORK DONE BY A VARIABLE FORCE

Work done is equal to the area under a force–distance graph.

What is the formula for work done by a simple spring?

$$W = \tfrac{1}{2}Fx = \tfrac{1}{2}kx^2$$

WATCH OUT
You must plot force up the y-axis, distance along the x-axis. Work done is the integral of force with respect to distance moved.

LINKS
For more information on force, extension and energy in typical solids, see pp. 23–24.

ENERGY CONVERSIONS

Roller coasters, ski slopes, pendulums, projectiles, etc., all provide ideal subjects to test your understanding of energy interconversions. Provided no energy is transferred to the surroundings (e.g. through friction), gravitational potential energy E_p lost = kinetic energy E_k gained (and vice versa). Write down equations for E_p and E_k.

$$E_p = mgh \qquad E_k = \tfrac{1}{2}mv^2$$

E_p is always a change in energy, not an absolute amount. Explain.

How does a car's braking distance depend on its speed?

Work done by brakes $(= Fs) = E_k$ lost $(= \tfrac{1}{2}mv^2)$.
If F is constant, braking distance $s \propto v^2$.

WATCH OUT
In an isolated system where mechanical energy is conserved, $E_k + E_p$ is constant. If you take the top of a roller coaster ride as $h = 0$, E_p will always be negative, which can cause confusion. Be crystal clear. Write things like: potential energy lost = kinetic energy gained.

EXAMINER'S SECRETS
The dependence of kinetic energy on v^2 is a favourite exam theme (and an important safety issue). At AS level, it is likely to be linked to the braking distance.

MOTIVE POWER

A vehicle's instantaneous power (its work rate) is equal to the driving force multiplied by the rate of movement, i.e.

$$P = Fv$$

WATCH OUT
The F in the power equation is the driving force, not the net resultant force. The same equation can be used to give braking power.

Turn the page for some exam questions on this topic ▶

EXAM QUESTION 1

A cyclist uses a constant net force of 160 N to accelerate from rest for 8.0 s on a flat road. If the mass of the cyclist plus their bicycle is 80 kg, calculate (a) their final speed, (b) their final kinetic energy, (c) the maximum height of hill they could free-wheel up (ignoring drag and friction).

(a) $a = 2\text{ m s}^{-2}$ so $v = 16\text{ m s}^{-1}$
(b) $E_k = 1.0 \times 10^4\text{ J}$
(c) $mgh_{max} = 1.0 \times 10^4 \Rightarrow h_{max} = 13\text{ m}$

EXAM QUESTION 2

(a) Calculate the kinetic energy of a car of total mass (with passengers and luggage) 1080 kg travelling at a speed of 80 km h^{-1}.

$80\text{ km h}^{-1} = 22\text{ m s}^{-1}$; $E_k = \tfrac{1}{2}mv^2 = 2.6 \times 10^5\text{ J}$

(b) The car's brakes provide a total braking force of 1600 N. If this is maintained throughout braking, what is the minimum braking distance?

$s = 2.6 \times 10^5/1600 = 160\text{ m (2 s.f.)}$

(c) Calculate the average power dissipated during braking.

$a = -1600/1080 = -1.5\text{ m s}^{-2} \Rightarrow$ time taken $= 15\text{ s}$
average power dissipated $= 2.6 \times 10^5/15 = 17\text{ kW}$

(d) What is the maximum power dissipated by the brakes? Why is this answer different from your answer to (c)?

$P_{max} = 1600 \times 22 = 35\text{ kW}$; instantaneous power depends directly on instantaneous speed

WATCH OUT
Speeds must be in m s^{-1} for all kinetic energy calculations.

DON'T FORGET
Average power is the total amount of work done divided by the total time taken.

EXAM QUESTION 3

The graph shows how a catapult's extension varies with the force applied.

(a) Calculate the energy stored when the extension is 120 mm.

Energy stored $=$ area under graph $= \tfrac{1}{2}F_{max}x_{max} = 1.8\text{ J}$

(b) Estimate the speed the catapult imparts to a 30 g missile.

$\tfrac{1}{2}mv^2 = 1.8 \Rightarrow v^2 = 3.6/0.030 \Rightarrow v = 11\text{ m s}^{-1}$

IF YOU HAVE TIME
Try calculating the force needed to propel the same missile at twice the speed.

EXAM QUESTION 4

A 600 kg powerboat is cruising at a steady 7.0 m s^{-1}. Its engine provides a constant driving force of 800 N. (a) What is the boat's power? (b) The fuel reserves amount to 12 MJ. For how long can the boat carry on at this speed?

(a) Power $= 5.6\text{ kW}$
(b) Boat can carry on for $2.1 \times 10^3\text{ s}$

IF YOU HAVE TIME
Calculate the maximum range of the boat assuming it continues travelling at 7 m s^{-1}. How could the driver increase his range?

Force, extension and energy for solids

Most materials obey Hooke's law within limits, making it one of the most important laws in engineering.

HOOKE'S LAW AND THE BEHAVIOUR OF SIMPLE SPRINGS

A spring is stretched to destruction. Sketch its force–extension curve.

Up to the limit of proportionality, Hooke's law is obeyed.

$$F = kx$$

Note that Hooke's law breaks down before permanent deformation (the elastic limit) is reached.

WATCH OUT
Extension is the extra length of the spring, not its total length.

Sketch the graph carefully. Show where Hooke's law breaks down; mark the elastic limit.

THE JARGON
The elastic limit is the limit beyond which permanent deformation occurs. It is not normally the point at which Hooke's law breaks down.

Write the symbol equation for Hooke's law.

ENERGY STORED IN A SPRING

The work done by a variable force is obtained from the area under a force–displacement curve. It is normally equal to the energy stored in the stretched spring.

Show that the energy stored in a simple spring is given by $E = \frac{1}{2}kx.x = \frac{1}{2}kx^2$.

Area of the triangle shown = $Fx = \frac{1}{2}kx.x = \frac{1}{2}kx^2$.

WATCH OUT
The graph is deliberately plotted in an unusual way. Extension depends on force, so extension would normally be plotted up the y-axis. But with force on the y-axis, the gradient of the graph gives the spring constant k and the area under the graph represents the energy stored.

EXAMINER'S SECRETS
Hooke's law for springs is covered at GCSE. It provides a useful introduction to this more general version.

LINKS
For a more detailed look at stress–strain curves, see pp. 25–26.

HOOKE'S LAW APPLIED TO MATERIALS

Within limits, stress is directly proportional to strain. Beyond the limit of proportionality, various strange things may happen.

Young's modulus = gradient

Energy density = area

Using the graph, how do you find the Young's modulus and the energy density (energy stored per unit volume) for the material?

Complete the table.

Quantity	Definition (words)	Symbols	Unit
Stress σ	force/area	F / A	Pa
Strain ε	extension/length	x / l	none
Young's modulus E	stress/strain	Fl / Ax	Pa

Turn the page for some exam questions on this topic ▶

For more on this topic, see pages 26–27 of the *Revision Express A-level Study Guide*

EXAM QUESTION 1

A certain spring has a spring constant of 0.20 N mm⁻¹. It is held vertically, unstressed. A 5.0 N weight is attached and the spring is released.

(a) What is the maximum distance the ball will fall?

Elastic potential gained at maximum fall = gravitational potential lost. E_p lost = $5.0 \times d$ (where d = max. fall).

Elastic E gained = $\frac{1}{2}kd^2$.

Applying conservation of energy, $d = 50$ mm.

(b) The spring is cut in half. What is the half-spring's spring constant? If the same weight were attached to the unstressed half-spring, what would be the maximum distance it would fall?

The half-spring must suffer half the extension under the same load, so k must be double that of the whole spring. $k = 0.40$ N mm⁻¹. Maximum fall is $d = 25$ mm.

Use conservation of energy to solve the problem. Be clear about your reasoning.

WATCH OUT
It is easy to make mistakes using intuition alone. When the calculations are simple, there is no excuse for cutting corners.

EXAM QUESTION 2

A bow manufacturer makes two types of bow: a simple bow (cheap) and a 'compound bow' (expensive). The graphs show how the force required varies as each bow is drawn towards full extension (0.5 m).

(a) Estimate or calculate the elastic potential energy of each bow at full extension.

Simple bow: $E = \frac{1}{2} \times 150 \times 0.5 = 38$ J (2 s.f.)

Compound bow: E = area under curve = 54 J

(b) What advantage does the compound bow offer?

The same (or more) energy can be stored using the same maximum force, with less effort at full extension. This makes steady aiming easier.

(c) Estimate the release speed of an arrow of mass 0.060 kg from the simple bow (from the fully extended position) assuming all the bow's elastic energy is transferred to the arrow as kinetic energy.

$\frac{1}{2} \times 0.06 \times v^2 = 38$ so $v = 35$ m s⁻¹

EXAMINER'S SECRETS
Always convert to SI units before doing long calculations, and check that your answers seem reasonable. Examiners try to make questions realistic. Suppose your answer to 2(c) were 350 m s⁻¹, you should be suspicious because arrows don't generally break the sound barrier.

EXAM QUESTION 3

A nylon fishing line has diameter 0.86 mm and length 1.50 m. If the Young's modulus of nylon is 3.7×10^9 Pa, find the line's extension when it supports a 16 N fish.

Cross-sectional area = 5.8×10^{-7} m²

Stress σ = 2.8×10^7 Pa; strain ε = 7.6×10^{-3}

Extension = ε × 1.50 = 1.1×10^{-2} m

© Pearson Education Limited 2001

Stress and strain

Understanding the behaviour of materials under stress is essential for good engineering and design.

TYPICAL STRESS–STRAIN CURVES

Stress–strain curves can be used to tell us the Young's modulus of a material, its energy density under stress, strength, flexibility, etc.

Which features of the steel graph show that high-carbon steel is stronger, stiffer and more brittle than mild steel?

Respectively, higher UTS, greater Young's modulus and less plastic flow beyond yield point.

The glass graph shows no plastic behaviour at all. Explain why.

Glass is amorphous – it has no crystal structure – so dislocations cannot move, making glass brittle.

Copper shows 'permanent set' beyond the yield point. Explain.

Ductile flow occurs as dislocations slip through crystal layers, causing a lengthening in the direction of tensile stress; this is permanent set.

Rubber is incredibly elastic. Explain why.

Rubber's elasticity occurs because it is a polymer; it consists of long molecules which are normally folded and have only weak cross-bonding.

The rubber graph also shows that the work done in stretching a rubber band is not equal to the elastic energy the band will repay on release. What happens to the excess energy used and what is the name of this effect?

The excess energy heats up the rubber as it is stretched. This effect is called hysteresis.

LINKS
For key definitions relevant to force, extension and energy, see pp. 23–24.

REVISION EXPRESS
A basic treatment of stress and strain is given on pp. 26–27 of the Revision Express A-level Study Guide; for more depth and detail, see the Study Guide sections on materials, pp. 164–169.

Revise key definitions and terms, study the graphs and answer the questions as fully as you can.

THE JARGON
Ultimate tensile stress (UTS) is the greatest stress a material can take before breaking.

THE JARGON
Yield stress is the stress at the elastic limit (where plastic behaviour starts).

THE JARGON
Limit of proportionality is the point where Hooke's law breaks down.

THE JARGON
Ductile flow is plastic behaviour beyond the yield point, where extra stress results in greatly increased strain, due to moving dislocations. Metals exhibit ductile flow.

THE JARGON
Creep is continued ductile flow when no extra stress is added.

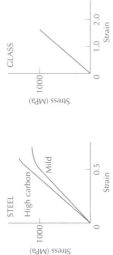

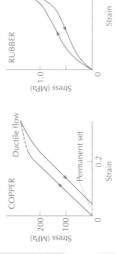

Turn the page for some exam questions on this topic ➤

EXAM QUESTION 1

A stress–strain graph is plotted for a wire stretched to breaking point.

(a) Calculate Young's modulus for the wire. Next find the metal's yield strain. Then find the metal's ultimate tensile stress (UTS).

$E = (12 \times 10^8)/(4.0 \times 10^{-3}) = 3.0 \times 10^{11}$ Pa

Strain at elastic limit $= 5.0 \times 10^{-3}$

UTS $= 1.5 \times 10^9$ Pa

(b) Describe what would have happened if the stress had been removed at points A, B and C.

A, B the wire would have returned to its original length (zero strain).

C the wire would have shown permanent set.

(c) Given that the wire's diameter is 1.5 mm and its length is 1.20 m, find the elastic potential energy of the wire at stress 6.0×10^8 Pa.

Area under the graph gives the wire's energy density, i.e. energy per unit volume

Area $= \frac{1}{2} \times 2.0 \times 10^{-3} \times 6.0 \times 10^8 = 6.0 \times 10^5$ J m^{-3}

Volume of wire $= \pi r^2 l = 2.12 \times 10^{-6}$ m^3

Energy $= 6.0 \times 10^5 \times 2.12 \times 10^{-6} = $ **1.3 J**

EXAMINER'S SECRETS
Make sure you know how to measure Young's modulus for a material. Simple explanations of experimental procedures can earn lots of easy marks. Think about the main sources of error and the best ways to minimize uncertainties.

DON'T FORGET
Strain is a ratio of two lengths, therefore it has no units.

EXAMINER'S SECRETS
Be prepared for questions based around load-extension graphs. You should know how to calculate stress, strain and Young's modulus from these graphs (given the diameter and length of the wire).

EXAM QUESTION 2

An engineer makes scale model cranes. The crane's lifting cables are made of high-tensile steel with UTS 1.6×10^9 Pa and the loads are solid cubic bricks of density 2000 kg m^{-3}.

(a) Calculate the maximum load each crane can lift.

Small model: $1.6 \times 10^9 \times \pi \times (2.0 \times 10^{-4})^2$
$= 201$ N

Large model: $4 \times 201 = 804$ N

(b) Work out if each crane can lift its load.

Small model: mass $= 16.0$ kg, weight $= 157$ N
$157 < 201$, so small crane can lift its load

Large model: mass $= 128$ kg, weight $= 1260$ N
$1260 > 804$, so large crane cannot lift its load

EXAMINER'S SECRETS
Scaling problems come up fairly frequently. A favourite is the maximum size of a land animal given that as size increases, weight (proportional to volume) increases more rapidly than supporting area.

Current as a flow of charge

Current is a flow of charge. In metals the charge carriers are electrons. Metals are good electrical conductors because they have lots of free electrons available to carry charge.

CONDUCTIVITY

Materials can be classified according to how well they conduct. Give a definition for insulators, semiconductors and conductors.

Insulators	Materials that don't contain charge carriers and so do not conduct
Semiconductors	Materials that conduct better with increasing temperature as more charge carriers are released
Conductors	Materials that contain many charge carriers and so conduct well

IF YOU HAVE TIME
Build up a bank of formulae used throughout this section.

CURRENT AS A RATE OF FLOW OF CHARGE

Current (I) and charge (Q) are related by $I = Q/t$ or $Q = It$.

Use $Q = I/t$ as a basis to calculate how much charge flowed in the 30 s illustrated by this graph.

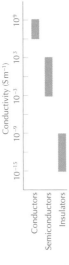

The area under the graph gives the amount of charge that flows.

In the first 10 s	charge = $0.5 \times 10 \times 5$	= 25 C
In the middle 10 s	charge = 10×5	= 50 C
In the last 10 s	charge = $0.5 \times 10 \times 5$	= 25 C
Total charge that flowed	= $25 + 50 + 25$	= 100 C

THE JARGON
A rate is a comparison of one quantity with another. In physics, a rate is normally a comparison against time, e.g. acceleration is a comparison of how quickly velocity changes with time.

Complete these equations.

CURRENT AND DRIFT VELOCITY

The current I in a metal wire is given by $I = nAev$, where n is the number of electrons per unit volume, A = cross-sectional area, e = charge carried by a free electron, v = drift velocity of free electrons.

Here are some estimates: $n = 10^{29}$ for copper at 20 °C, $A = 8 \times 10^{-7}$ m² say for a wire, $e = -1.6 \times 10^{-19}$ C and $v = 1$ mm s^{-1} typically.

SOME COMMON CIRCUIT SYMBOLS

Name the circuit component that each symbol represents.

variable resistor   LED

fuse   ammeter

thermistor   voltmeter

earth

Turn the page for some exam questions on this topic ▶

EXAM QUESTION 1

This chart gives conductivity values for three groups of materials.

Use the chart to help you begin answering this question.

Conductivity (S m^{-1})

| 10^{-15} | 10^{-9} | 10^{-3} | 10^3 | 10^9 |

Conductors
Semiconductors
Insulators

(a) What is the minimum conductivity of a conductor?

10^6 S m^{-1}

(b) What happens to the conductivity of semiconductors with increasing temperature?

It increases.

(c) Why does the conductivity of semiconductors vary in this way?

At absolute zero (−273 °C) all the outer shell electrons in a semiconductor are used to form covalent (electron sharing) bonds between atoms. As the temperature rises, more and more of these electrons break free and can carry charge, so the semiconductor's conductivity increases.

EXAM QUESTION 2

A variety of experiments can be used to support the theory that current is a flow of charge, e.g. conduction by coloured salts.

(a) Suggest three other pieces of evidence that support this theory.

Kirchhoff's first law
Operation of a TV tube
Shuttling ball demonstration

(b) Describe an experiment to show conduction by coloured salts.

LINKS
For Kirchhoff's laws, see pp. 35-36.

Draw a diagram to illustrate your answer.

Describe a method, suggest a set of observations and offer a conclusion.

+25 V

Large pin

Potassium permanganate crystal

Microscope slide

Negative terminal of power supply

Filter paper is soaked in ammonia solution and then placed on a microscope slide. Pins are placed on the filter paper and connected to the power supply. A potassium permanganate crystal is dropped on the filter paper and the power is switched on. Negatively charged permanganate ions drift slowly to the positive pin, showing a connection between current and movement of charged particles.

Current, p.d. and resistance

For a current to flow through a conductor, a potential difference (p.d.) must be applied across it. If a conductor with a higher resistance is used, less current will flow for the same p.d.

ENERGY TRANSFERS

> Electrons are joule (jewel) thieves; they transfer precious energy. Use arrows to link each partial statement with the appropriate ending.

1 Batteries are a store of — light energy
2 When electrons pick it up, it is then — electrical energy
3 As electrons move, it is considered as — thermal energy
4 Electrons transfer energy to resistors as — chemical energy
5 Light bulbs convert ≤ 5% of energy into — kinetic energy

⑤ ② ④ ① ③

> **IF YOU HAVE TIME**
> Start to make a list of all the physical quantities used in this topic, together with their symbol and unit.

POTENTIAL DIFFERENCE

> Identify each of the correct statements in this list with a T for true or an F for false.

Potential difference (p.d.) is the scientific name for voltage — T

Potential difference is measured in volts (V) where $1\,V = 1\,J\,C^{-1}$ — T

Potential difference is measured using a voltmeter in series — F

The potential difference between two points is the electrical energy converted into other forms when 1 C of charge passes between them — T

The potential differences across bulbs in parallel add up to the potential difference of their supply — F

The potential difference between two points is the energy transferred in moving +1 C of charge between them — T

> **WATCH OUT**
> Don't confuse the definition of the volt ($1\,V = 1\,J\,C^{-1}$) and the definition of the amp ($1\,A = 1\,C\,s^{-1}$).

SERIES AND PARALLEL CIRCUITS

> Electrical components can be connected in series or parallel. Write down whether each statement is true for series circuits only, for parallel circuits only, or for both types of circuit.

Electrons give up all their energy before returning to the power supply — both

The current is the same at every point — series only

There must be at least one complete path to allow current to flow — both

The electrons have more than one possible route available to them — parallel only

Turn the page for some exam questions on this topic ▶

For more on this topic, see pages 62–63 of the *Revision Express A-level Study Guide*

EXAM QUESTION 1

This circuit contains four identical lamps. (a) Which lamps will be the brightest? (b) Which lamps will have the greatest current flowing through them? (c) What type of meter is X? (d) Add an arrow to the diagram to show the direction in which conventional current leaves the battery. Label this arrow C.

Brightest: 1
Greatest current: 1
Meter X is an ammeter

EXAM QUESTION 2

The **resistance** of a component tells us about how much **current** will flow through it for a given **voltage**.

Define then explain the physical origins of the words in bold.

> **WATCH OUT**
> This question uses the term 'voltage', now considered vague and old-fashioned. Use p.d. and e.m.f. as a way to clarify the meaning of voltage in your answer.

> Complete this table.

	Symbol	Equation	Unit	Unit definition
Resistance	R	$R = V/I$	Ω	$1\,\Omega = 1\,V\,A^{-1}$
Current	I	$I = Q/t$	A	$1\,A = 1\,C\,s^{-1}$
Voltage	V	$V = W/Q$	V	$1\,V = 1\,J\,C^{-1}$

Free electron — Lattice of positive ions — Lattice vibrations increase with temperature

> Fill in the missing labels on this diagram.

Resistance — As free electrons move through a metal wire, they collide with each other and with positive ions in the wire. Some of their energy is transferred to the wire, which then becomes hotter. This is the basis of resistance

> Give a short explanation of the physical origin of each of these terms.

Current — Current is a flow of charged particles

Voltage — There are two types of voltage. An electromotive force (e.m.f.) involves transfer of energy to charged particles. A potential difference involves transfer of energy from charged particles

> **EXAMINER'S SECRETS**
> Electromotive force is really a misnomer. It is not a force at all. It describes an energy change where energy is transferred to charge.

Resistors and resistivity

(AS) AQA-A AQA-B CCEA EDEXCEL OCR-A OCR-B WJEC

The resistance of a wire indicates how hard it is for electrons to flow through it. Length, cross-sectional area, temperature and material all affect resistance.

OHM'S LAW

The current through a conductor is proportional to the p.d. across it, provided the temperature of the conductor remains constant.

Water to keep the wire at a constant temperature

p.d. (V)	I (A)	R (Ω)
2.0	0.5	4.0
4.0	1.0	4.0
6.0	1.5	4.0

Rearrange $V = IR$ to make R the subject of the equation, then complete the table of results for this experiment.

For each set of measurements quoted above, what can you say about potential difference divided by current?

It always has the same value (here it is 4.0 Ω).

If p.d. doubles then what happens to I? I doubles.

How are I and p.d. related? I is proportional to p.d.

Answer these questions to reach the conclusion for this experiment.

FACTORS AFFECTING RESISTANCE

The results of the previous experiment have been plotted in the following graph and labelled A.

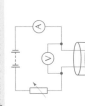

Label both axes on this graph.

Add a second line to show a set of results that might be obtained from a wire of greater resistance; label this line B.

The resistances of two different wires are not always the same.

$$R = \rho l/A$$

Note the equation that shows the factors affecting the resistance of a wire at constant temperature.

RESISTORS IN SERIES AND PARALLEL

Series: $R_{total} = R_1 + R_2 + R_3$ Parallel: $1/R_{total} = 1/R_1 + 1/R_2 + 1/R_3$

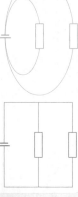

$$1/R_t = \frac{1}{4} + \frac{1}{4}$$
$$= \frac{1}{2}$$
$$R_t = 2\,\Omega$$

Redraw this circuit to show more clearly how to construct it in practice. Then calculate R_{total} (R_t) if $R_1 = R_2 = 4\,\Omega$.

Turn the page for some exam questions on this topic ▶

EXAM QUESTION 1

The resistance of a thermistor varies with temperature.

(a) Describe the relationship illustrated by this graph.

As temperature increases, the resistance of this thermistor falls in a non-linear way. The change in resistance is approximately exponential.

(b) Thermistors are non-ohmic. Describe what this means and give two other examples of non-ohmic electrical components.

A non-ohmic device does not obey Ohm's law; the current through it isn't proportional to the p.d. across it. Diodes and filament lamps are also non-ohmic conductors.

(c) Sketch a graph to show how the p.d. across a thermistor varies with the current I through it.

WATCH OUT

Read questions carefully. If you're asked to plot a graph of I against p.d., I should be on the y-axis and p.d. should be on the x-axis.

EXAM QUESTION 2

A student is asked to determine the resistivity of a 20 cm long pencil lead (a compound of graphite and clay). They are then required to calculate the thickness of a pencil line drawn with this pencil lead.

(a) The student sharpened both ends of the pencil and found that the resistance of the lead was $5.1 \times 10^{-3}\,\Omega$. If the diameter of the lead was 2.00 mm, what was its resistivity?

$R = \rho l/A$ so $\rho = RA/l$
$= 5.1 \times 10^{-3}[\pi \times (1 \times 10^{-3})^2]/0.2$
$= 8.0 \times 10^{-8}\,\Omega\,m$

(b) The student used the pencil to draw a uniformly thick line, 30 cm long and 2 mm wide. Using an ohmmeter, they found the line to have a resistance of 600 Ω. What was the thickness of the pencil line?

$R = \rho l/A$ so $A = \rho l/R =$ width × thickness = wt

30 cm

$A = wt = 0.002t$

$t = \rho l/Rw = (8.0 \times 10^{-8} \times 0.3)/(600 \times 0.002)$
$= 2 \times 10^{-8}\,m$

DON'T FORGET

Show your method whenever you do a calculation.

EXAMINER'S SECRETS

Marks are often allocated for units, so don't forget to state them in your final answer.

EXAM QUESTION 1

The cell below has negligible internal resistance and the bulbs are identical.

5.0 Ω 5.0 Ω 6.0 V 5.0 Ω 5.0 Ω
4.0 Ω 4.0 Ω 4.0 Ω

(a) Calculate the current flowing through each bulb.

Series circuit, so $R_t = R_1 + R_2 + R_3 + R_4$
$= 5 + 5 + 4 + 4 = 18 \ \Omega$

Using $V = IR$ *gives* $I = V/R = 6/18 = 0.33$ A

(b) Calculate the power dissipated in each bulb.

$P = I^2R = (0.33)^2 \times 4 = 0.44$ W

(c) Calculate the amount of energy changed into other forms by each bulb in 2.0 minutes.

Power = (energy changed)/(time taken)
So $E = Pt = I^2Rt = 0.44$ W $\times 2 \times 60$ s $= 53$ J

- Highlight the most important parts of this paragraph.
- Why are these parts significant?

EXAM QUESTION 2

'Quick blow' fuses are used to protect a variety of delicate electrical devices. You are asked to test one such fuse to check its maker's claim that **it blows within 5 ms of the current rising above 3 A. Design an experiment to carry out this task.**

A time of 5 ms is much quicker than human reaction time (typically 0.1–0.4 s). Stopwatch methods that rely on humans switching the timer on and off will be inappropriate. In addition, the circuit must provide a way to vary the current.

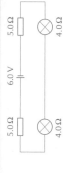

A

Gradually decrease the resistance while video recording the fuse and ammeter

- Draw a circuit diagram of your experiment.

By recording the experiment and then playing back the tape in slow motion, frame by frame, it would be possible to determine the time taken by the fuse to blow after the current reached 3 A. It would simply be a matter of counting how many frames elapsed between the current reaching 3 A and the fuse blowing. Suppose each frame lasted 1 ms and the event took place within 5 frames, then the maker's claims would have been verified.

- Describe your method and how you would use your results to reach a conclusion.

IF YOU HAVE TIME
Rewrite this answer using a different method, e.g. by using an oscilloscope (CRO) or high-speed photography. Remember to consider the CRO's time base or the camera's shutter speed in your answers.

Electrical energy and power

AQA:A AQA:B CCEA EDEXCEL OCR:A OCR:B WJEC

Electricity can be used to transfer energy. Electrons are used to 'pick up' and 'drop off' packets of energy. Power tells us how quickly energy is changed from one form to another.

THE JARGON
A complete circuit has two parts: the internal circuit (inside the power supply) and the external circuit (bulbs, resistors, etc.).

ENERGY TRANSFORMATIONS

In complete circuits, energy changes occur in the power supply or in the external circuit.

In the power supply	From chemical energy (in a cell) into electrical energy (of electrons)
In the external circuit	From electrical energy into heat energy (e.g. in a resistor)

- Give an example of these energy transfers.

POWER EQUATION $P = VI$

1.5 V ⎓ 2 A

1 V is defined as	$1 \ J \ C^{-1}$
Here each coulomb of charge entering the cell gains	1.5 J
1 A is defined as	$1 C \ s^{-1}$
Here the number of coulombs entering and leaving the cell every second is	2 C
Power is defined as	energy changed per second
As 2×1.5 J leave the cell every second, the power is	3 W

- Complete these statements to explain why $P = VI$.

SYLLABUS CHECK
Some courses expect you to be able to check that equations are homogeneous. If this is so for your course, check $P = VI$ and $P = I^2R$.

THE JARGON
Dissipate means to scatter. Energy changes in an external circuit usually involve heating, so they are irreversible. Therefore 'dissipate' is a good word to use.

POWER DISSIPATED $P = I^2R$

Statement	True/false	Correction (if needed)
$P = VI$ is used for power gains	True	
To transmit at high power, use high V or low I	False	High V and high I
$P = I^2R$ is used for energy losses	True	
When transmitting at high power it does not matter whether V or I is large	False	Power losses are proportional to I^2, so a large I loses lots of P
It's not possible to transmit at high power and minimize power losses	False	Use high V and low I

- Complete this table to see how electricity is transmitted by the national grid.

DON'T FORGET
$P = VI$ can be used when power is lost or gained by electrons. $P = I^2R$ is only used when electrons lose power.

Turn the page for some exam questions on this topic ▶

For more on this topic, see pages 68–69 of the *Revision Express A-level Study Guide*

EXAM QUESTION 1

Use Kirchhoff's first law to find values for the currents a to g.

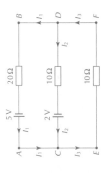

Working from the top left and moving clockwise ...
First junction: 12 mA = a + 8.4 mA, so a = 3.6 mA.
Second junction: current rejoins, so b = 12 mA.
Third junction: current splits again but as 9.5 mA flows through bottom resistor, d = 9.5 mA, then 12 = c + 9.5, so c = 2.5 mA.
This 2.5 mA splits into e and 1.5 mA, so e = 1 mA.
All the currents then rejoin, so f = g = 12 mA.

EXAM QUESTION 2

Use Kirchhoff's first law (K1) and Kirchhoff's second law (K2) to calculate values for I_1, I_2 and I_3.

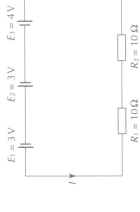

Apply K1 at junction C	$I_1 + I_2 = I_3$	[1]
Apply K2 to loop CEFD		
Substitute $I_3 = I_1 + I_2$	$2 = 10I_3 + 10I_2$	
	$2 = 10(I_1 + I_2) + 10I_2$	[2]
	$2 = 10I_1 + 20I_2$	
Apply K2 to loop AEFB	$5 = 10I_3 + 20I_1$	
Substitute $I_3 = I_1 + I_2$	$5 = 10(I_1 + I_2) + 20I_1$	
	$5 = 30I_1 + 10I_2$	[3]
[3] × 2	$10 = 60I_1 + 20I_2$	[4]
[4] − [2]	$8 = 50I_1$	
Simplifying	$I_1 = 0.16$ A	
Substitute for I_1 in [2]	$2 = (10 \times 0.16) + 20I_2$	
	$20I_2 = 0.4$	
	$I_2 = 0.02$ A	
Solve [1]	$I_3 = 0.16 + 0.02 = 0.18$ A	

WATCH OUT
You are often asked to put in your own arrows to show current direction. If at the end of your calculation one of your values for current is a negative number, the minus sign indicates that the current flowed in the opposite direction to the way you guessed.

SYLLABUS CHECK
Questions like this are not set by all boards, e.g. AQA:A and AQA:B. The solution to this type of question involves the use of simultaneous equations.

Kirchhoff's laws

(AS) AQA:A AQA:B CCEA EDEXCEL OCR:A OCR:B WJEC

Kirchhoff's laws allow current and voltage to be calculated at any point in a circuit. They are consequences of conservation of charge and energy within electrical circuits.

KIRCHHOFF'S FIRST LAW

B = ?
B = 10 A
E = ?
E = 12 A
C = ?
C = 4 A
D = 6 A
D = ?

Kirchhoff's first law says that the (algebraic) sum of the currents into a point equals the (algebraic) sum of the currents out of that point. Use Kirchhoff's first law to calculate the currents B, C, D and E.

THE JARGON
Here the word 'algebraic' means that the directions of the currents have to be taken into account.

KIRCHHOFF'S SECOND LAW

$\Sigma E = \Sigma IR$ is a mathematical expression of Kirchhoff's second law.

$E_1 = 3 V$ $E_2 = 3 V$ $E_3 = 4 V$
$R_1 = 10 \Omega$ $R_2 = 10 \Omega$

$\Sigma E = 3 + 3 + (-4) = 2 V$
$\Sigma IR = 10I + 10I = 20I$
$\Sigma E = \Sigma IR \Rightarrow 2 = 20I$ so $I = 0.1$ A

Kirchhoff's second law says that the (algebraic) sum of the e.m.f.s in any closed loop in a circuit is equal to the (algebraic) sum of the p.d.s around that loop.

SYLLABUS CHECK
Kirchhoff's second law is not required by CCEA.

SYLLABUS CHECK
Check whether your course will set questions involving the use of simultaneous equations.

Complete this calculation.

CONSERVATION LAWS

Kirchhoff's first law is a consequence of ...	conservation of energy because ...	electrons do not disappear.
Kirchhoff's second law is a consequence of ...	conservation of charge because ...	energy gained by the electrons from the power supplies is lost in the resistors.

Shade to form complete sentences that match Kirchhoff's laws.

LINKS
For more on e.m.f., see pp. 39–40.

Turn the page for some exam questions on this topic ▶

Potential dividers and their uses

The term 'potential divider' describes a circuit in which resistors divide a battery's voltage. Potential dividers are often used with transistors to form electronic control circuits.

PRINCIPLE OF POTENTIAL DIVIDERS

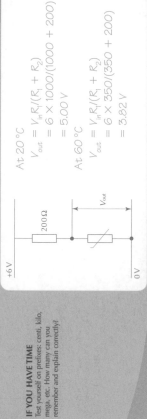

Circuit 1

$V_{in} = 6\,V$

R_1 $2\,\Omega$ V_{out}

R_2 $10\,\Omega$ V_2

V_{out} can be altered if a variable resistor is used as R_2

Circuit 2

V_{in}

R_1, R_2

V_{out}

Circuit 3

V_{in}

R_1

V_{out}

R_2

Wire of fairly high resistance per unit length, e.g. constantan

$V_{out} = V_{in}R_1/(R_1 + R_2) = 6 \times 2/(2 + 10) = 1\,V$

WATCH OUT
The term 'potential divider' is a little misleading. Perhaps 'potential difference divider' would more accurately describe these circuits.

THE JARGON
The term 'potentiometer' can be used to describe an instrument for measuring p.d. or e.m.f. It can also refer to a variable resistor (as shown in circuit 2) that can be used to tap off a variable p.d.

Potential dividers can portion off a small voltage from a larger one. Use this formula to calculate V_{out}.

IF YOU HAVE TIME
Redraw circuit 3 replacing the constantan resistance wire with a number of resistors in series. Then you should be able to see how V_{out} can be varied.

Potential dividers often form the heart of automatic control circuits. If circuit 2 were to be used in this way, what advantages and limitations would it have? Jot down some ideas in the table opposite.

Advantages	Limitations and drawbacks
V_{out} can be varied by moving the slider	Some current flows through R_1 and R_2 so some power is wasted
Good control of V_{out} from 0 to maximum	Can be tricky to connect
A transistor could be connected across V_{out} to act as a switch	Relies on human to move slider, so not automatic

REAL USES OF POTENTIAL DIVIDERS

List some practical uses of potential dividers.

Temperature control, e.g. baby incubator
Temperature monitor, e.g. automatic fire alarm
Automatic light switch
Volume control on a radio
Controls for brightness and contrast on a TV

Turn the page for some exam questions on this topic ▶

For more on this topic, see pages 70–71 of the *Revision Express A-level Study Guide*

EXAM QUESTION 1

The thermistor used in this circuit has a resistance of $1000\,\Omega$ at $20\,°C$. Its resistance falls to $350\,\Omega$ when it is heated to $60\,°C$. Calculate V_{out} at $20\,°C$ and $60\,°C$.

+6V

$200\,\Omega$

V_{out}

0V

At $20\,°C$

$V_{out} = V_{in}R_1/(R_1 + R_2)$
$= 6 \times 1000/(1000 + 200)$
$= 5.00\,V$

At $60\,°C$

$V_{out} = V_{in}R_1/(R_1 + R_2)$
$= 6 \times 350/(350 + 200)$
$= 3.82\,V$

IF YOU HAVE TIME
Test yourself on prefixes: centi, kilo, mega, etc. How many can you remember and explain correctly?

EXAM QUESTION 2

A student used a small value rheostat, connected as shown, to plot an I–V characteristic graph for an LED.

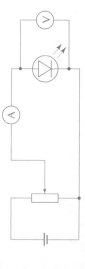

(a) What are the advantages of this arrangement over connecting the rheostat in series with the ammeter?

It offers a greater range of I and V. It also allows fine control over the range of applied p.d.

(b) Why might the student's choice of a small value rheostat be a problem in the circuit that has been constructed?

Their choice of a small value rheostat may be a problem because the entire supply p.d. is across it. If a large current flows through a small section of the rheostat, the rheostat could overheat.

THE JARGON
Rheostat is another name for a variable resistor.

WATCH OUT
Say 'a small value rheostat', not 'a small rheostat'. A rheostat that provides relatively small resistances may not necessarily have a small volume.

EXAM QUESTION 3

Explain how a potential divider could be used in a real-life application of your choice (e.g. as part of a car's fuel gauge).

A float is connected to a potential divider via a rod and rests on the surface of the fuel in a car's tank. As the fuel level changes, the float's position varies too. This changes the position of the sliding contact within the potential divider. The output voltage from the potential divider is altered and this alters the fuel gauge readout.

e.m.f. and internal resistance

Electromotive force is the energy available per unit charge to produce current. Internal resistance is the resistance provided by a source of e.m.f. as charge passes through it.

ELECTROMOTIVE FORCE

○○○

SYLLABUS CHECK
CCEA does not require details of cells and measurement of internal resistance.

The e.m.f. of this cell is 3 V

The switch is open so there is no current

IF YOU HAVE TIME
Compile a glossary of key scientific words used in this section. Try to limit each explanation to one sentence.

The switch is now closed so there is a current

INTERNAL RESISTANCE

The electrons pick up energy as they pass through the cell, but the chemicals in the cell also provide some internal resistance.

	Simple symbol	Advanced symbol

Sketch a more advanced symbol for a cell showing that cells provide internal resistance. Use this symbol from now on whenever a cell is assumed to have internal resistance.

Source of e.m.f.	Internal resistance caused by
Cell (or battery of cells)	Resistance of the cell's electrolytes and electrodes
Power pack (transformer)	Electrical resistance of wires within power pack

Complete this table.

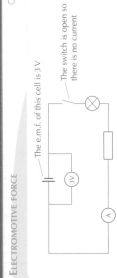

$R_{total} = R_1 + R_2 = R + r$

$= 4 + 2 = 6\,\Omega$

$V = IR$ so $I = V/R$

Here $I = E/(R + r)$

so $I = 12 / (4 + 2) = 2\,A$

Complete this example to calculate the current flowing in the circuit and the reading on the voltmeter.

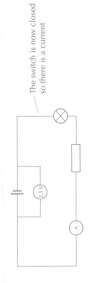

$E = 12\,V$ $r = 2\,\Omega$

$V = ?$

$I = ?$

$R = 4\,\Omega$

p.d. across cell terminals = p.d. across resistor R

$V = IR$ (for resistor R) $= 2 \times 4 = 8\,V$

DON'T FORGET
Note that r causes terminal p.d. to drop when there is a current.

Turn the page for some exam questions on this topic ▶

For more on this topic, see pages 72–73 of the *Revision Express A-level Study Guide*

EXAM QUESTION 1

○○○

A friend has been absent for several lessons and asks you to explain the main effects of 'internal resistance'.

- Internal resistance limits the current in a circuit.
- When a current is produced, some of the energy transferred to the charge as it passes through the cell is 'lost' ('lost volts') due to internal resistance (a voltmeter connected across the terminals will record a reading less than the e.m.f. of the cell).
- The flow of charge through the internal resistance heats the cell.
- The terminal p.d. of a cell falls as the current rises (terminal p.d. = e.m.f. – 'lost volts' = $E - Ir$, so as I increases, Ir increases, so terminal p.d. falls).

WATCH OUT
The terminal p.d. (i.e. the p.d. across the terminals of the cell) equals the p.d. across the external resistors, not the 'lost volts' across the internal resistance of the cell.

EXAM QUESTION 2

○○○

E $r = 2\,\Omega$

$R = 20\,\Omega$

$I = 0.5\,A$

(a) Calculate the 'lost volts', the cell's terminal p.d. and its e.m.f.

'lost volts' $= Ir = 0.5 \times 2 = 1\,V$

terminal p.d. $= IR = 0.5 \times 20 = 10\,V$

terminal p.d. $=$ e.m.f. – 'lost volts'

e.m.f. $=$ terminal p.d. + 'lost volts'

$= 10 + 1 = 11\,V$

(b) Describe qualitatively how this circuit could be changed to make the terminal p.d. have a value closer to the e.m.f. of the cell.

The external resistor R should be replaced with a resistor of higher resistance.

(c) Why would your change in part (b) have the desired effect?

By increasing the total resistance in the circuit, the current I would decrease; this would decrease the 'lost volts' Ir. As terminal p.d. $= E - Ir$, the terminal p.d. would approach E, the cell's e.m.f.

(d) What kind of voltmeter should be used to measure the e.m.f. of a power supply? Explain your answer.

A high-resistance voltmeter, e.g. a digital voltmeter with resistance at least 1 MΩ, should be used. Then only a small current will flow through it, so the 'lost volts' will be a tiny fraction of the power supply's e.m.f.

DON'T FORGET
The terminal p.d. of a cell is equal to its e.m.f. only when no current is flowing.

For more on this topic, see pages 98–99 of the *Revision Express A-level Study Guide*

EXAM QUESTION 1

(a) Explain the meaning of mechanical transverse and mechanical longitudinal waves.

Mechanical transverse waves need a medium to travel through. They are caused by vibrations at 90° to the wave's motion and transmit energy by passing mechanical vibrations from particle to particle. Mechanical longitudinal waves are similar but they are caused by vibrations moving in the same direction as the wave's motion.

(b) Give one example of each type of wave in part (a).

Mechanical transverse: ripples caused by a stone being dropped at 90° into a pond
Mechanical longitudinal: sound wave

(c) What is meant by polarization?

Polarization is the process by which certain waves can be forced to oscillate in one fixed direction only.

(d) Why is it that only transverse waves and not longitudinal waves can be polarized? Illustrate your answer with diagrams if possible.

This is a tricky question; try to base your answer on a simple demonstration.

EXAMINER'S SECRETS
As the question suggests using a diagram, some marks may only be obtainable this way. In other words, do a diagram or lose marks.

Picket fence
Slinky (a)
Slinky (b)
Vibration
Vibration

Two slinky springs are threaded through a picket fence and vibrated as shown. The longitudinal wave sent along slinky (a) passes through the fence, but the transverse wave in slinky (b) cannot pass through because of the vertical fence posts. The posts will only allow a transverse wave to pass if it is caused by vibrations in the vertical plane. It is not possible to polarize longitudinal waves because they only vibrate in the direction of the wave motion.

EXAM QUESTION 2

Circle the letter beside the one statement that is incorrect.

SYLLABUS CHECK
AQA:A uses multiple choice questions. Check the types of question set by your exam board.

All waves carry energy	A
Electromagnetic waves can be polarized	B
Only transverse waves can be diffracted	C
Waves propagate by progressive local displacement of a medium or a change in its physical properties	D

Types of waves and their properties

Waves are vibrations that carry energy. Some waves, e.g. sound, need a medium to travel through; others, e.g. light, do not. Waves never involve an overall movement of matter.

CLASSIFYING WAVES: SIX TERMS

Jot down some notes about each type of wave shown here.

IF YOU HAVE TIME
Illustrate each wave type with an example.

SPEED LEARNING
Use a mnemonic to remember different wave types: **P**erry **M**ason **s**olves **l**egal **t**angles **e**asily (progressive, mechanical, stationary, longitudinal, transverse, electromagnetic).

Wave classification	Notes
Transverse	caused by vibrations at 90° to direction of the wave's motion
Longitudinal	caused by vibrations in same direction as the wave's motion
Mechanical	transmit energy by passing mechanical vibrations from particle to particle
Electromagnetic	transmit energy as oscillating electric and magnetic fields
Progressive	spread energy from the source vibration into the surrounding space
Stationary or standing	have nodes and antinodes that do not change position

DESCRIBING WAVES

Wavelength
Amplitude
Displacement

This diagram represents a side-on view of a transverse wave. Add some labels.

Add arrows to this table to match each term with the correct definition. Write the correct unit in the right-hand column. The unit for speed has been entered for you.

	Term	Definition or equation		Unit
1	Frequency	Time for one complete vibration	③	Hz
2	Amplitude	Number of vibrations per second	①	m
3	Period	Maximum displacement	②	s
4	Displacement	Distance between point on wave and line of zero disturbance	④	m
5	Wavelength	Frequency × wavelength	⑥	m
6	Speed	Distance between two adjacent points that are in phase	⑤	m s^{-1}

WAVE EQUATION

The wave equation is $v = f\lambda$. A wave travels at speed $v = 0.40 \text{ m s}^{-1}$, and its frequency is $f = 5.0$ Hz. What is its wavelength λ?

$$\lambda = v/f = 0.40/5.0 = 0.08 \text{ m}$$

Turn the page for some exam questions on this topic ▶

Reflection and refraction

(AS) AQA:A AQA:B CCEA OCR:A OCR:B WJEC

When waves or particles are reflected, the angle of incidence equals the angle of reflection. Waves refract (change direction) if they change speed when entering a new medium at a slanting angle.

THE LAWS OF REFLECTION

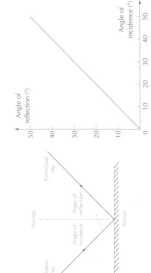

Normal · Incident ray · Reflected ray · Angle of incidence · Angle of reflection · Mirror

Angle of reflection (°) vs Angle of incidence (°)

(1) The angle of incidence equals the angle of reflection.
(2) The normal, incident and reflected rays all lie on the same plane.

Label the diagram, then sketch the results that would be obtained. Use the graph provided.

IF YOU HAVE TIME
Find out about the travelling microscope and how it can be used to determine the refractive index of a glass block.

Make a note of the laws of reflection.

THE LAWS OF REFRACTION

(a) refractive index $_1n_2$ = $\dfrac{\text{speed of light in medium 1}}{\text{speed of light in medium 2}}$

(b) n_1 = $\dfrac{\text{speed of light in a vacuum}}{\text{speed of light in medium 1}}$

(c) $_1n_2$ = $\dfrac{\sin i}{\sin r}$

(d) $_1n_2$ = $\dfrac{\text{real depth}}{\text{apparent depth}}$

(e) $_1n_2$ = n_2/n_1

(f) $_2n_1$ = $1/_1n_2$

Which law is used to calculate the absolute refractive index?
Which law is named after Willebrod Snell?

Choose from (a)–(f) to answer these two questions.

This diagram shows a ray of light entering glycerol from air. Complete the calculation to find the refractive index of glycerol:

$_1n_2$ = $\dfrac{\sin i}{\sin r}$ = $\dfrac{\sin 44.5°}{\sin 28.5°}$ = 1.47

Air · 44.5° · 28.5° · Glycerol

(b)
(c)

Turn the page for some exam questions on this topic ▶

For more on this topic, see pages 102–103 of the *Revision Express A-level Study Guide*

EXAM QUESTION 1

Using a wavefront diagram, explain why refraction occurs when light enters an optically denser medium at an angle other than 90°.

Light waves move more quickly through air
Air–water boundary
Light waves move more slowly through water

This side of the wavefront reaches the water first and slows down first, making the light beam bend or refract

WATCH OUT
Optical density has nothing to do with mass/volume.

Sketch and label a wavefront diagram to provide your answer.

EXAM QUESTION 2

Ultrasound imaging can be used to measure the precise depth of a structure within the body, e.g. the position of the midline of the brain. Each peak (1–4) in this CRO trace shows the position of a reflecting surface. The height of each peak represents the amplitude of the echo received.

Signal strength vs Time — peaks 1, 2, 3, 4

(a) Which peak corresponds to the deepest structure? Say why.

Peak 4: this was the last peak to be formed, so the ultrasound waves travelled furthest to produce it.

(b) Which peak corresponds to the most reflective surface? Say why.

Peak 2: this peak had the highest signal strength.

(c) Can ultrasound be refracted? Give a reason for your answer.

Yes, refraction is a property of all waves.

SYLLABUS CHECK
Some courses, e.g. OCR:B, expect you to interpret physics that is new to you. Some exams, e.g. some set by AQA:B, include questions based on a scientific passage.

EXAM QUESTION 3

The refractive index for light travelling between air and diamond is taken to be 2.42.

If a light ray enters diamond at an angle of 30.0°, calculate the angle of refraction.

$\sin r = \dfrac{\sin i}{n} = \dfrac{\sin 30°}{2.42} = 0.207$ so $r = 11.9°$

What is the refractive index for light escaping from diamond into air?

$_2n_1 = 1/_1n_2$ so $_dn_a = 1/2.42 = 0.413$

Show your method clearly.

Total internal reflection and fibre optics

AQA:A AQA:B CCEA OCR:A OCR:B WJEC

Fibre optics are sometimes called 'light pipes'. Light is trapped within them, bouncing along by total internal reflection (TIR). They can convey information encoded as flashes of light.

IF YOU HAVE TIME
Examiners are influenced in the choice of question they set by events or articles reported in the media. Make a habit of keeping up to date yourself.

Add rays to each of these diagrams to illustrate refraction, the critical angle and total internal reflection.

TOTAL INTERNAL REFLECTION AND THE CRITICAL ANGLE

The critical angle C is the angle of incidence i that produces an angle of refraction equal to 90°. If $i > C$ the ray is totally internally reflected.

Normal — Air / Glass — $i < C$

Normal — Air / Glass — $i = C$

Normal — Air / Glass — $i > C$

The refractive index of borosilicate is 1.474. To find the critical angle for a ray of light in borosilicate, start with $n = 1/\sin C$.

Complete the calculation.

FIBRE OPTICS

Fibre optics use the principle of TIR in a variety of applications.

List some uses of fibre optics.

Fibre optics have many advantages.

Now list some advantages.

Fibre optics rely on total internal reflection.

Label this diagram.

Maximum angle of incidence

CHECK THE NET
If you're interested in how things work, then why not ask a professor of physics? Go to http://landau1.phys.virginia.edu/Education/Teaching/HowThingsWork

Turn the page for some exam questions on this topic ▶

For more on this topic, see pages 104–105 of the *Revision Express A-level Study Guide*

EXAM QUESTION 1

A prism is made from light flint glass of refractive index 1.578.

(Diagram showing prism with angles 45°, 45° and Ray R)

(a) Calculate the critical angle for a ray of light in this material.

$\sin C = 1/n = 1/1.578 = 0.6337$
$C = \sin^{-1} 0.6337 = 39.32°$

(b) Use your answer to part (a) to complete the path of ray R through the prism. Show your answer on the diagram above.

(c) Explain why refractive indices do not have units.

A refractive index is a ratio that indicates how much bending will occur when a ray travels from one medium into another, e.g. n equals the speed of light in medium 1 divided by the speed of light in medium 2. Therefore it does not have a unit.

EXAM QUESTION 2

Describe an experiment to measure the critical angle for light at a Perspex–air boundary.

(Diagram labelled: Paper, Normal, Refracted ray, Semicircular Perspex block, Reflected ray, Angle of incidence, Incident ray)

Draw a labelled diagram.

The block is placed on a sheet of paper. Its outline is traced to mark its position. The block is then removed and a normal is drawn at the point where the centre of its flat surface will lie. The block is replaced and a ray of light is directed towards it as shown on the diagram. The angle of incidence is increased until the refracted ray just disappears. The path of the incident ray is marked with two crosses so that a permanent record of it can be drawn. This incident angle (the critical angle C) is measured with a protractor. The experiment is repeated at least three times, then an average value for C is obtained. Substitute this average value into the equation $\sin C = 1/n$ to obtain a value for the refractive index n.

Explain the method and describe what you expect to happen. Finally, show how you will use your results to find the value of C.

EXAMINER'S SECRETS
There may be only four marks available for question 2 (one for the apparatus, two for the method and one for your analysis). Use the number of marks available to determine how long you spend on each question.

Diffraction

AS AQA:B CCEA OCR:A OCR:B WJEC

Diffraction is the spreading out of a wave as it passes through a gap or around an obstacle.

GAP WIDTH, WAVELENGTH AND DIFFRACTION

The extent to which waves are diffracted depends upon their wavelength and the width of the gap they are passing through.

Complete these wavefront diagrams to show what happens in the spaces beyond the gaps.

IF YOU HAVE TIME
Start to make your own revision cards on the following wave properties: reflection, refraction, diffraction and interference.

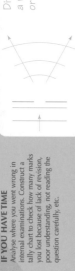

very little disturbance

Maximum diffraction occurs when the gap width is equal to the wavelength of the waves.

What can be concluded from the diagrams?

SINGLE-SLIT DIFFRACTION OF LIGHT WAVES

A very narrow slit can be used to diffract monochromatic laser light.

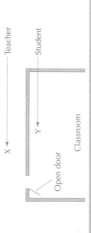

Adjustable slit

Photographic film

Laser

Intensity

Position on screen

0

The diffracted light was captured on a photographic film. An analysis of this film is shown above. Position 0 was directly ahead of the slit.

There are bright and dark regions on the film.
The central fringe is twice as wide as the others.
The central fringe is much brighter than the others.

Study the graph and write down any conclusions you can draw from it.

DIFFRACTION OF MICROWAVES

Transmitter

Metal plates

For maximum diffraction, gap width = 4 cm

Receiver

Direction of movement

Meter

The microwaves in this demonstration have a wavelength of 4 cm. Add labels to this diagram.

Turn the page for some exam questions on this topic ▶

For more on this topic, see pages 106–107 of the *Revision Express A-level Study Guide*

EXAM QUESTION 1

(a) **Use a diagram to explain what is meant by diffraction.**

Diffraction is the spreading out of a wave as it passes through a gap or around an obstacle.

(b) **A classroom door has been left open. The diagram shows the positions of a quiet student in the classroom and a teacher talking outside. Use your knowledge of diffraction to explain why the student can hear but not see the teacher.**

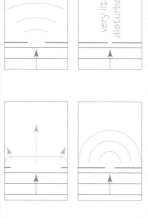

Teacher

Student

X

Y

Open door

Classroom

The condition for maximum diffraction is that the gap width should equal the wavelength of the incoming waves. The wavelengths of sound waves have the same order of magnitude as the width of a doorway, so the sound waves from the teacher are significantly diffracted as they pass into the classroom. This lets the student hear the teacher. As the wavelength of light waves is very much less than the width of the door opening, light reflecting off the teacher is not significantly diffracted or spread into the classroom. This means it would not be possible for the student to see the teacher.

EXAM QUESTION 2

How could you show that the degree of water wave diffraction depends upon the relative sizes of gap width and wavelength?

I could use a ripple tank, plane dipper, electric motor and two barriers. I could send plane waves of constant wavelength towards the gap between the two barriers, then I could observe the degree of diffraction. Keeping a constant wavelength for the incoming water waves, I could alter the gap width and make further observations on the degree of diffraction. Alternatively, I could keep the gap width constant and vary the wavelength of the incoming water waves.

IF YOU HAVE TIME
Analyse where you went wrong in internal examinations. Construct a tally chart to check how many marks you lost because of lack of revision, poor understanding, not reading the question carefully, etc.

LINKS
To see a diagram of the equipment used in this experiment, see p. 51.

Superposition

AS AQA:B CCEA OCR:A OCR:B WJEC

Superposition means placing one figure upon another. The principle of superposition can be applied to all waves and was used by Christian Huygens to support his wave theory of light.

THE PRINCIPLE OF SUPERPOSITION

When waves cross, the total displacement at a point equals the sum of the individual displacements at that point.

crest + crest → supercrest
trough + trough → supertrough
crest + trough → zero

Complete these flow diagrams to show how crests and troughs form supercrests and supertroughs or cancel to zero.

Complete the diagrams to show the result of each superposition.

DON'T FORGET
Super revision depends upon the magic five. You should repeat your learning five times: within an hour, a day, a week, a month and then after three months.

Displacement–time graphs

Displacement

→ Time

KEY TERMS

Explain each of these terms.

In phase	Waves that vibrate in step
In antiphase	Waves totally out of step, i.e. crests of one coincide with troughs of another
Path difference	Extra distance that one set of waves travels compared with another
Bright fringe	Region where crests of light waves arrive with other crests, forming supercrests
Dark fringe	Region where crests of light waves arrive with troughs, cancelling each other out

Turn the page for some exam questions on this topic ▶

For more on this topic, see pages 108–109 of the *Revision Express A-level Study Guide*

EXAM QUESTION 1

(a) 'The **superposition** of light waves from **coherent** sources can produce **interference** effects.' Explain the words in italics.

There is no need to use diagrams here.

Superposition is the act of two or more vibrations (or waves) combining to produce a single vibration (or wave). Coherent sources produce waves that have a constant phase difference.

(b) Is it possible to superpose two waves of different wavelengths to produce an interference pattern? Include diagrams in your answer.

You need some diagrams here.

Yes, it is possible, as shown in the diagrams.

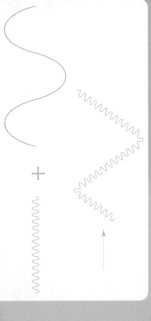

EXAM QUESTION 2

(a) 'Superposition involves vector addition.' Explain this statement.

Superposition involves adding displacements. As displacement is a vector quantity (it's the distance an object moves from its rest position in a given direction), combining two waves involves taking account of direction as well as magnitude.

(b) State one practical application of superposition.

Many messages can be passed down a single optical fibre as light waves, then 'disentangled' at the other end.

EXAMINER'S SECRETS
Many exam questions contain clues. Read the whole question and find the clues.

IF YOU HAVE TIME
List some other practical applications of superposition.

(c) Look at the diagram, then add to it the wave that would be produced by superposition of the two original waves.

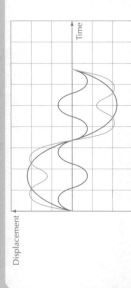

Displacement

→ Time

Interference

AS AQA/B CCEA OCR:A OCR:B WJEC

Interference occurs when waves combine by superposition. The result of interference is an observable pattern if there is a constant phase difference between waves of similar amplitude.

USING A RIPPLE TANK TO OBSERVE INTERFERENCE

Dipper suspended from crossbar — Electrical supply — Motor to make vibrations — Gaps — Plane wavefronts — Overlapping waves — Absorber e.g. iron wool — Ripple tank — Water

Add labels to this diagram.

EXAMINER'S SECRETS
Try to include details that show you have actually performed the experiment, e.g. an absorber to cut down unwanted reflections from the walls of the ripple tank.

List two other pieces of equipment often used with the ripple tank. Explain their functions.

Apparatus	Use
Stroboscope	Helps to make the interference pattern more clearly visible
Lamp	Placed above or below the tank to project interference patterns on the floor or ceiling

YOUNG'S DOUBLE-SLIT EXPERIMENT – UPDATED

Laser — Diffraction occurs at both slits — Double slits — Interference occurs in this region — Screen

Note the reasons for using a laser.

A laser is used for two main reasons
(1) It provides coherent waves from both slits
(2) It produces light of a single wavelength, known as monochromatic light

Note the two main conclusions.

There are two main conclusions
(1) Constructive interference produces bright fringes and destructive interference produces dark fringes
(2) Light can be explained by a wave theory

Turn the page for some exam questions on this topic ▶

For more on this topic, see pages 110–111 of the *Revision Express A-level Study Guide*

EXAM QUESTION 1

In a Young's double-slit experiment, light of wavelength 0.54×10^{-6} m was incident upon a pair of parallel slits of separation 0.50 mm. The fringes were viewed on a screen that was 90 cm from the slits. Calculate the distance between consecutive bright fringes.

Write down the correct formula, show your working and highlight your answer.

We have that $\lambda = ax/D$
where λ = wavelength = 0.54×10^{-6} m
a = slit separation = 0.50 mm
x = fringe separation
D = slit-to-screen distance = 90 cm

So $x = \lambda D/a$
$= (0.54 \times 10^{-6} \times 0.9)/(0.50 \times 10^{-3})$
$= 9.7 \times 10^{-4}$ m

EXAM QUESTION 2

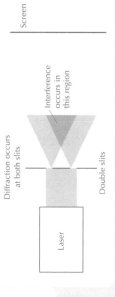

Loudspeaker — Loudspeaker

This diagram shows a way to study interference of sound waves.

(a) Assuming that an interference pattern was established, what would you notice if you walked along the line *AB*?

I would pass through loud and quiet regions.

(b) What is constructive interference and how could you recognize a region formed by constructive interference?

Constructive interference describes overlapping waves that reinforce each other. I could use loudness to recognize a region formed by constructive interference; it would be loud because it occurs where crests arrive with other crests.

(c) Add three lines to the diagram to show where constructive interference occurs.

See the diagram.

(d) What is the name given to the semicircular lines in the diagram and what do they indicate?

They are called wavefronts and they indicate the position of compressions.

(e) Suggest two sets of equipment that could be used to detect loud and quiet regions in an experiment such as this.

Use a microphone connected to a cathode ray oscilloscope (CRO) or use a decibelmeter.

EXAMINER'S SECRETS
AS questions tend to be qualitative (you have to describe something) whereas A2 questions tend to be more quantitative (you have to calculate something).

IF YOU HAVE TIME
Compile a concept map to summarize the material you have covered in this section.

S1 Standing waves

AS AQA/B CCEA OCR:A OCR:B WJEC

Standing waves occur when two waves of equal wavelength and amplitude and travelling in opposite directions cross and combine by superposition.

EXPLAINING STANDING WAVES

The diagrams show two waves travelling in opposite directions. The initial situation is shown in part (a). Subsequent moments are shown in parts (b), (c) and (d).

Add arrows to (c) and (d) showing how the two waves continue to move in opposite directions.

Consider the line labelled A. It shows the position of an antinode, where the amplitude of the combined wave varies a lot. Draw another line, to the right of this one, showing the position of the next antinode.

(a)

(b)

(c)

(d)

N   A   A

Complete these sentences.

At all points labelled N, the waves interfere .... destructively.

The combined amplitude at these points is always .... zero.

These points are called .... nodes.

The positions of nodes (and antinodes) always remain .... constant.

Adjacent nodes (or adjacent antinodes) are separated by .... λ/2.

IF YOU HAVE TIME
Look again at the first three sentences then write similar ones for the points labelled A.

STANDING WAVE PATTERNS

Standing waves, or stationary waves, are often demonstrated with sound waves, microwaves or stretched strings as shown here.

Draw the next two possible standing wave patterns. Include arrows to show the direction of movement of adjacent sections of the strings.

Fundamental frequency or first harmonic — λ/2

First overtone or second harmonic — λ

Second overtone or third harmonic — 3λ/2

Complete these sentences.

The fixed points at the ends of the string are always .... nodes.

Adjacent nodes are separated by .... λ/2.

Adjacent sections of the string move in opposite .... directions.

Turn the page for some exam questions on this topic ▲

For more on this topic, see pages 112–113 of the *Revision Express A-level Study Guide*

EXAM QUESTION 1

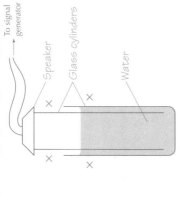

To signal generator

Speaker

Glass cylinders

Water

DON'T FORGET
Apparatus diagrams are conventionally simplified with symbols such as the crosses shown here. Crosses represent clamp stands.

IF YOU HAVE TIME
Staple some rough paper together. If you know your stuff, you should be able to make up questions on this topic. Now try answering them.

This apparatus was used to investigate standing waves.

(a) Add the missing labels to the diagram.

(b) How would you find the first position at which resonance occurs?

I would adjust the signal generator to say 300 Hz, then I'd raise the inner tube until the sound was loudest. This would be the first resonance position.

(c) Why is a loud sound generated here?

Sound waves from the speaker are reflecting off the water surface. A standing wave has been set up. The waves from the speaker are constructively interfering with the reflected waves, forming an antinode at the top of the inner tube.

(d) How does the length of the air column, contained in the inner tube at this position, compare with the wavelength of the sound?

The length of the air column equals λ/4.

(e) The inner tube is raised and the loudness of the sound changes. How far is the tube raised before the sound reaches its loudest level again? Quote your answer as a fraction of λ.

The tube is raised a distance λ/2.

EXAM QUESTION 2

Two microwave transmitters, producing waves of the same wavelength and frequency, are set up facing each other about 1.0 m apart. A receiver is moved around in the region between them and it is found that points of minimum intensity are separated by 1.4 cm. Calculate the wavelength and frequency of the microwaves. Assume the speed of electromagnetic waves, $c = 3.0 \times 10^8$ m s^{-1}.

Remember to include relevant formulae and units. Show your method clearly.

Distance between nodes = λ/2 = 1.4 cm   so λ = 2.8 cm

Now $c = f\lambda$ so $f = c/\lambda$
$= (3.0 \times 10^8)/(2.8 \times 10^{-2})$
$= 1.1 \times 10^{10}$ Hz

© Pearson Education Limited 2001

Planck's constant

Classical physics could not explain how very hot objects emit radiation or why electrons do not spiral into the nucleus. The work of Max Planck held the key to a new, quantum era.

LIMITATIONS OF CLASSICAL PHYSICS ○○○

THE JARGON
Classical physics can be thought of as nineteenth-century physics.

List four things that classical physics cannot explain.

Things that are too big
Things that are too small
Things that are too hot
Things that go too fast

THE ULTRAVIOLET CATASTROPHE ○○○

One classical law that couldn't withstand close scrutiny was the Rayleigh–Jeans law. This related the intensity I of electromagnetic radiation, at wavelength λ, to the temperature T of a black body. It suggested that if temperature remains constant then $I \propto 1/\lambda^4$.

THE JARGON
A black body is a perfect emitter and absorber of electromagnetic radiation. Stars are black bodies.

Plot two graphs on the axes provided, one showing how intensity really varies with wavelength and one showing the trend predicted by Rayleigh–Jeans.

Rayleigh–Jeans law
Observed spectrum

Intensity / Wavelength

Compare the graphs you have drawn. Now complete these conclusions.

The Rayleigh–Jeans law worked only at _____ long wavelengths

Rayleigh–Jeans did not predict _____ a lower wavelength limit

The catastrophe was that _____ classical physics could not explain these failings

THE JARGON
An empirical expression is obtained from experiment and observation, instead of from theory.

MAX PLANCK'S SOLUTION ○○○

Planck knew that standing wave patterns could be established on vibrating strings only at certain frequencies. Sketch the three most basic patterns.

Planck explained how black bodies emit electromagnetic (EM) radiation by studying the observed spectrum and producing an expression that agreed with it.

$3f$

$2f$

f

Planck's idea suggested that the energy of an oscillator comes in whole number multiples of hf. Sketch these quantized energy levels.

Planck suggested that charged particles also can vibrate only at certain frequencies (to emit EM radiation). He suggested that the energy of an oscillator is proportional to its frequency, giving $E = hf$.

$E = 3hf$

$E = 2hf$

$E = hf$

Turn the page for some exam questions on this topic ▶

For more on this topic, see pages 114–115 of the *Revision Express A-level Study Guide*

IF YOU HAVE TIME
Construct a time line showing key events in the development of quantum theory.

EXAM QUESTION 1

Before the twentieth century, physicists could not explain how stars emit electromagnetic (EM) radiation. This question is about Max Planck's contribution to a better understanding of the phenomenon.

(a) What was already known about the emission of EM radiation?

It was already known that vibrating charged particles, e.g. electrons, produce EM radiation.

(b) What incorrect assumption had been made by physicists?

They assumed that the charged particles could oscillate at any frequency.

(c) How did Planck use another area of physics to correct this?

He suggested that charged particles could vibrate only with certain frequencies. According to Planck, charged particles are like vibrating strings as they have a certain number of fixed frequencies that can produce standing wave patterns.

(d) Before 1900 it was suggested that the relationship between the intensity I of EM radiation and its wavelength λ was $I \propto 1/\lambda^4$, as long as the temperature remained constant. Suppose this is true, then what would happen to I as λ decreases?

Assuming the relationship is true, I would become infinite at low values of λ.

(e) What actually happens to the intensity of EM radiation at low wavelengths?

As λ decreases, I increases to a maximum. If λ decreases further then I decreases, eventually reaching zero.

(f) How did Planck explain the lower wavelength limit?

Planck used the similarity between vibrating charged particles and oscillating strings to show that there would be an upper limit to the frequency of the radiation. This meant there would be a lower limit to its wavelength.

(g) How was this work extended to suggest that energy comes in small packets or quanta?

Planck showed that the energy E of an oscillator is proportional to its frequency f, so $E = hf$. Here h is Planck's constant and it equals 6.63×10^{-34} J s. As Planck had proposed that only certain frequencies were possible, $E = hf$ suggested that there are only certain allowable values for E.

The photoelectric effect

AS AQ:A CCEA OCR:A OCR:B WJEC

The photoelectric effect is the ejection of electrons from a metal by a beam of sufficiently energetic (ultraviolet) radiation. The very nature of light had to be re-evaluated to explain it.

WATCH OUT
The idea that light has a dual nature (wave-particle duality) is a very difficult concept for most students.

SYLLABUS CHECK
CCEA candidates are required to know how Planck's constant can be determined experimentally. This 'stopping potential' experiment is not covered here.

DEMONSTRATING THE PHOTOELECTRIC EFFECT

Ultraviolet radiation
Clean zinc plate
Gold leaf electroscope

Label this diagram.

The method is very simple:

Use a high-voltage power supply to give the electroscope a negative charge.
Shine ultraviolet radiation (from a mercury lamp) towards the zinc plate.

Make a note of the method.

Here are the observations:

The leaf rises when given the initial charge.
The leaf falls when the ultraviolet radiation reaches the zinc plate.

List the observations.

We can draw two conclusions:

Charging the electroscope gave it an excess of electrons. The ultraviolet radiation helped these electrons to escape, so the leaf lost its charge and fell down.

State the conclusions that can be drawn.

EXPLAINING THE PHOTOELECTRIC EFFECT

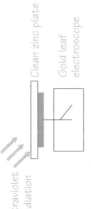

Photon $E_1 = hf_1$ ($E_1 > W$) — Electron escapes

Photon $E_2 = hf_2$ ($E_2 = W$) — Electron reaches surface

Photon $E_3 = hf_3$ ($E_3 < W$) — No electron emitted

Complete each of these diagrams to show what happens. *W* is the work function.

Turn the page for some exam questions on this topic ▶

For more on this topic, see pages 116–117 of the *Revision Express A-level Study Guide*

EXAM QUESTION 1

(a) State the meaning of each term in Einstein's photoelectric equation
$$KE_{max} = hf - W.$$

KE_{max} = maximum kinetic energy of photoelectrons
h = Planck's constant (6.63×10^{-34} J s)
f = frequency of incident light
hf = photon energy
W = work function

WATCH OUT
KE_{max} has been used here but you may well see the symbol E_{kmax} used instead.

(b) Sketch a graph of KE_{max} against f.

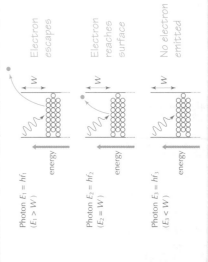

(c) Explain how h and W can be obtained from a graph like this.

h = the gradient of the graph.
$-W$ = the intercept on the *y*-axis.

EXAMINER'S SECRETS
Examiners will be checking to see how well you can analyse the graphs you draw. Part (c) is testing your analytical skills.

EXAM QUESTION 2

(a) What is the photoelectric effect?

It is the emission of (photo)electrons from the surface of a metal illuminated by sufficiently energetic electromagnetic (EM) radiation.

(b) Why was the wave theory of light unable to explain this effect?

Electrons are not emitted unless the incoming photons are sufficiently energetic (are above a threshold frequency, as $E = hf$). The wave theory suggested that even very weak incident radiation would eventually release an electron.
The wave theory implied that brighter light would allow electrons to escape with greater kinetic energy (KE). KE_{max} depends on frequency, not intensity.
The wave theory could not explain how a very weak beam of high-frequency EM radiation could release electrons almost instantaneously.

(c) How did Einstein explain the photoelectric effect?

Einstein suggested that EM radiation reached the metal in packets of energy. He said that the energy of each packet was proportional to the frequency of light used ($E = hf$). Einstein proposed that each packet of energy is given to just one electron in the metal. If the electron is sufficiently weakly bound to the metal, it will be released. Any excess energy not used to break it free will reappear as its kinetic energy.

For more on this topic, see pages 118–119 of the *Revision Express A-level Study Guide*

EXAM QUESTION 1

(a) According to classical physics, what would happen to an electron that emitted radiation as it orbited a nucleus?

The energy loss would cause the electron to spiral into the nucleus.

(b) Who explained the emission line spectra for hydrogen? Briefly describe their explanation.

Niels Bohr explained the emission line spectra for atomic hydrogen. He suggested that a hydrogen atom could exist in one of a set of energy levels. Radiation would be emitted if the atom moved from one energy level to a lower state. The radiation would be carried away by a single photon.

EXAM QUESTION 2

When white light passes through a gas, the continuous spectrum is found to have a few dark lines across it.

(a) What causes these dark lines?

The gas absorbed photons of specific energy from the white light. Each absorbed photon delivered the right amount of energy to lift an electron within the gas from one energy level to a higher level.

(b) How could the gas in question be identified?

Elements are characterized by the energy levels available to their electrons. Therefore they are also characterized by the jumps their electrons can make between energy levels. Consequently, this gas could be identified by the photons it absorbed.

EXAM QUESTION 3

Calculate the frequency of the spectral line caused by electrons changing from level 4 to level 2 in this energy level diagram.

Level	Energy (eV)
4	−0.85
3	−1.5
2	−3.4
1	−6.2

Energy loss $= (-0.85) - (-3.4) = 2.55$ eV
$= 2.55 \times 1.6 \times 10^{-19} = 4.08 \times 10^{-19}$ J
$E = hf$
$f = (4.08 \times 10^{-19})/(6.63 \times 10^{-34})$
$= 6.15 \times 10^{14}$ Hz

DON'T FORGET
An electron-volt (eV) is a unit of energy. To convert from joules to electron-volts, divide by 1.6×10^{-19}. To convert from electron-volts to joules, multiply by 1.6×10^{-19}.

EXAMINER'S SECRETS
Examiners try to construct mark schemes that reward good physics rather than penalizing poor maths. In this question you could still get two marks out of three even if you didn't convert from electron-volts into joules before using $E = hf$.

Atomic line spectra

AS AQA:A AQA:B CCEA OCR:B WJEC

Electrons within atoms can absorb and emit radiation. Atoms can be identified by studying the wavelengths their electrons absorb or emit. Classical physics failed to explain spectra.

SYLLABUS CHECK
Check whether your syllabus requires details of each series or just the principle of how they are formed.

EMISSION SPECTRA EXPLAINED

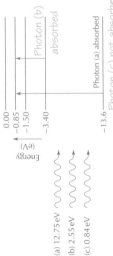

This energy level change produces a very energetic photon

This is a slightly simplified energy level diagram for a hydrogen atom. The Balmer series and the Paschen series are formed when electrons fall to energy levels $n = 2$ and $n = 3$ respectively. Complete this diagram to show these series.

Photons are emitted when electrons fall from one energy level to another. Use the diagram to show which lines in the Balmer and Paschen series produce the most energetic photons.

ABSORPTION SPECTRA EXPLAINED

Energy (eV): 0.00, −0.85, −1.50, −3.40, −13.6

Photon (b) absorbed
Photon (a) absorbed
Photon (c) not absorbed

(a) 12.75 eV
(b) 2.55 eV
(c) 0.84 eV

An atom can absorb a photon if it delivers exactly the right amount of energy to lift an electron from one energy level to another.

Add to this diagram to show what happens to photons (b) and (c).

PHOTON ENERGIES

The energy of the photon, emitted or absorbed, is equal to the difference between the two energy levels involved ($E = hf = E_1 - E_2$).

$E = hf = E_1 - E_2$
$= [-5.44 - (-21.8)] \times 10^{-18}$
$= 16.4 \times 10^{-18}$ J

$f = E/h$
$= (16.4 \times 10^{-18})/(6.63 \times 10^{-34})$
$= 2.47 \times 10^{16}$ Hz

$\lambda = c/f$
$= (3.00 \times 10^{8})/(2.47 \times 10^{16})$
$= 1.21 \times 10^{-8}$ m

Energy × 10⁻¹⁸ (J): −5.44, −21.8

Calculate the energy of the photon emitted when an electron falls from one energy level to another as shown in the diagram. Calculate the frequency and wavelength of the emitted radiation.

Turn the page for some exam questions on this topic ▶

Wave–particle duality

The natural world is beautifully symmetrical. In 1924 Prince Louis de Broglie proposed that if radiation has a dual, wave-particle nature, perhaps matter has a 'split personality' too.

LINKS
For more on the photoelectric effect, see pp. 57–58.

THE PARTICLE NATURE OF EM WAVES

In 1905 Einstein explained the photoelectric effect by assuming that light sometimes behaves as if its energy comes in packets or quanta.

Complete this table to show whether the phenomenon is explained by the wave theory or the quantum (particle) theory.

Phenomenon	Explanatory theory
Diffraction	wave
Interference	wave
Polarization	wave
Photoelectric effect	quantum (particle)
Line spectra	quantum (particle)

THE WAVE NATURE OF PARTICLES

In 1924 de Broglie suggested that radiation was not unique; matter (e.g. electrons) could also have both wave and particle properties.

De Broglie began with the formula for the momentum of a photon:
momentum = h/c

We also have that $c = f\lambda$, which can be rearranged with λ as subject:
$\lambda = c/f$

Taking the reciprocal gives $1/\lambda = f/\lambda$, which allows us to rewrite (1) as
momentum = h/λ (1)

Then rearranging to make λ the subject:
$\lambda = h/momentum$

De Broglie speculated that this applies to both particles and photons.
Particles have momentum mv, so we can write
$\lambda = h/mv$

This is called the de Broglie wavelength.

Complete this derivation to show how de Broglie argued that particles might have wave-like properties.

That he may sometimes have missed the target in his speculations, as for example in his theory of light quanta, cannot really be held against him.
MAX PLANCK
(REFERRING TO ALBERT EINSTEIN)

TESTING WHETHER PARTICLES HAVE WAVE PROPERTIES

This diagram shows an experiment similar to that used by George Thomson (son of J.J. Thomson) to prove that diffraction occurs in the foil.

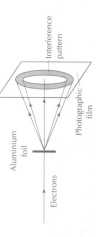

Electrons
Aluminium foil
Photographic film
Interference pattern

[It] seems at present to be wholly untenable.
ROBERT MILLIKAN
(WRITING OF EINSTEIN'S PHOTON THEORY)

It proved that electrons behave in a wave-like manner in this situation.

Say what this experiment proved.

Turn the page for some exam questions on this topic ►

For more on this topic, see pages 120–123 of the *Revision Express A-level Study Guide*

EXAM QUESTION 1

(a) What is meant by wave–particle duality?

This refers to the dual nature of both matter and radiation. Waves sometimes exhibit properties associated with particles, and particles display wave-like properties in certain circumstances.

(b) A student suggests that when considering particles, only charged particles (e.g. electrons) exhibit a dual nature. Is this true or false?

False: all particles, charged or uncharged, have a dual nature.

(c) How does de Broglie's equation show the dual nature of particles?

De Broglie's equation is $\lambda = h/p$ (= h/mv). It shows the duality of particles as wavelength λ is a wave property whereas momentum p is associated with particles. Planck's constant h seems to link the dual nature of both matter and radiation.

IF YOU HAVE TIME
Examine a list of Nobel prizewinners in physics between 1901 and 1945. Pick out the discoveries or contributions you are already familiar with. This will remind you of the progress you are making in your study of physics.

EXAM QUESTION 2

(a) Calculate the de Broglie wavelengths of (i) a car of mass 1000 kg moving at 70 km h⁻¹ and (ii) an electron of mass 9.1×10^{-31} kg moving at 1.0×10^{7} ms⁻¹.

$\lambda_{car} = h/m_{car}v_{car}$
$= (6.6 \times 10^{-34})/[1.0 \times 10^{3} \times 70 \times 10^{3}/(60 \times 60)]$
$= 3.4 \times 10^{-38}$ m

$\lambda_{electron} = h/m_{electron}v_{electron}$
$= (6.6 \times 10^{-34})/(9.1 \times 10^{-31} \times 1.0 \times 10^{7})$
$= 7.3 \times 10^{-11}$ m

(b) Is it easier to observe duality using a car or an electron? Explain the reason for your choice.

When a wave passes through a gap, significant diffraction occurs if the gap width is approximately the same size as the wavelength of the wave. The electron's de Broglie wavelength is comparable to the spacing of atoms in a crystal (10^{-10} m), so it is easier to observe duality using an electron.

EXAMINER'S SECRETS
Be careful to avoid ambiguous or unclear answers. Examiners do not read ideas into a candidate's answer; they only mark what they have in front of them.

EXAM QUESTION 3

Describe how electron diffraction gives evidence for the wave nature of particles.

When electrons strike a layer of atoms, e.g. graphite or aluminium, they are diffracted into a characteristic pattern of rings visible on a fluorescent screen or photographic film. Faster electrons have more momentum and smaller wavelengths, and they diffract less.

Radioactivity

Radioactivity is caused by spontaneous nuclear reactions.

BACKGROUND RADIATION

Definition	Ionizing radiation from the surroundings (which cannot or has not been avoided)
Sources	The Sun, naturally occurring radioactive rocks and gases, cosmic rays

Define background radiation and suggest some of its sources.

DON'T FORGET
Always use the word 'ionizing' to describe the radiation from a radioactive source.

TYPES OF IONIZING RADIATION

Radiation	Description	Z	A
α	high-energy helium nucleus	2	4
β−	high-energy electron	−1	0
β+	high-energy positron	+1	0
γ	high-energy photon	0	0

Place α, β and γ in order of penetrating ability $\gamma > \beta > \alpha$

Place α, β and γ in order of (local) ionizing ability $\alpha > \beta > \gamma$

EXAMINER'S SECRETS
Any radioactivity question based on a standard practical will test whether you know how to deal with background radiation over a reasonably long period, then subtract it from the counts.

THE JARGON
A positron is an electron's antiparticle. It has exactly the same mass as an electron, but it is positively charged.

THE EFFECT OF DIFFERENT DECAYS ON Z, N AND A

Decay	Effect on Z	Effect on N	Effect on A
α	−2	−2	−4
β−	+1	−1	0
β+	−1	+1	0
γ	0	0	0

Here N is the neutron number. But in the next section N is the number of radioactive atoms remaining. Take care to check what symbols mean.

IF YOU HAVE TIME
Get some practice with nuclear equations. Try writing equations for the decay of a general element by each type of decay (e.g. $^A_Z X \rightarrow {}^{A-4}_{Z-2}X + {}^4_2\alpha$).

RADIOACTIVE DECAY

Activity is the rate of decay from a source and its unit is the becquerel: 1 Bq = 1 decay per second.

Activity of a radioactive source is proportional to the number N of radioactive atoms remaining: $A = \lambda N$. λ is called the decay constant. Does λ increase or decrease with increasing instability?

It increases; λ is a measure of instability.

Decay constant λ is related to radioactive half-life ($t_{1/2}$) by the equation $\lambda t_{1/2} = 0.693$. What is radioactive half-life?

The average time taken for a source's activity to halve (decay reduces radioactivity).

Define activity and give its unit.

RADIOACTIVE DATING

Radioactive decay can be used as a clock. What three quantities do you need to work out the age of a radioactive source?

Its initial activity, its present activity and its half-life (or decay constant).

EXAMINER'S SECRETS
Here is a common question: How could you measure a radionuclide's half-life? The link with the decay constant allows a similar question to be asked in a new way, so be prepared.

Turn the page for some exam questions on this topic ➤

For more on this topic, see pages 44–49 of the *Revision Express A-level Study Guide*

EXAM QUESTION 1

(a) What is meant by radioactive half-life?

The time for a source's activity to fall by one-half.

(b) A certain sealed-source beta emitter is known to have a half-life of a few hours. Describe how you might determine its half-life. State all safety precautions.

Use a suitable detector (e.g. a G-M detector). Measure background radiation. Measure count rates from the source every 10 minutes. Subtract background from all counts. Plot corrected count rates against time. Find the time for count rates to halve from at least two regions along the best-fit curve. Safety: use tongs, keep your distance, direct source away, don't leave unattended.

(c) Another radionuclide is known to have a much longer half-life. Given that a certain source contains 1.7×10^{15} atoms of this nuclide and has an activity of 4.0×10^7 Bq, calculate its decay constant and hence find its half-life.

$$A = \lambda N \Rightarrow \lambda = (4 \times 10^7)/(1.7 \times 10^{15}) = 2.4 \times 10^{-8}\ \text{s}^{-1}$$
$$t_{1/2} = 0.693/\lambda = 2.9 \times 10^7\ \text{s}$$

EXAMINER'S SECRETS
This is a standard experiment. Questions may focus on practicalities, safety or ways of improving accuracy. Random errors can be minimized by obtaining counts as large as possible, but long counting periods may introduce systematic errors.

EXAM QUESTION 2

The graph shows the N–Z curve for stable nuclides. Three radionuclides are found in positions A, B and C.

(a) What is the likely decay mechanism for each radionuclide? Explain your reasoning.

(A) β⁻, (B) α, (C) β⁺. These mechanisms increase stability (daughter is closer to the stable N–Z line).

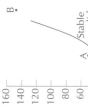

(b) A, B and C are actually $^{90}_{38}$Sr, which decays to Y, $^{238}_{92}$U, which decays to Th, and $^{22}_{11}$Na, which decays to Ne. Write balanced equations for their decay.

$$^{90}_{38}\text{Sr} \rightarrow {}^{90}_{39}\text{Y} + {}^{0}_{-1}\beta + \nu$$
$$^{238}_{92}\text{U} \rightarrow {}^{234}_{90}\text{Th} + {}^{4}_{2}\alpha$$
$$^{22}_{11}\text{Na} \rightarrow {}^{22}_{10}\text{Ne} + {}^{0}_{1}\beta^{+} + \nu$$

(c) Uranium-238 also emits gamma rays. Would you expect them to be monoenergetic (all the same energy) or not?

Yes, α-particles are monoenergetic, so their associated γ-rays are also monoenergetic.

EXAMINER'S SECRETS
The N–Z curve (or A–Z curve) also tells us that as Z increases, nuclei need extra neutrons to space out the protons. Another common exam theme is the relative range of the strong force of attraction between all nucleons and the Coulomb repulsion between protons.

SYLLABUS CHECK
Check whether your syllabus requires neutrinos (and antineutrinos). If in doubt, it's probably wise to include them.

DON'T FORGET
Single-energy rays suggest quantum energy leaps, and this is powerful support for quantum theory.

The nuclear atom

What *is* everything made of?

THE NUCLEAR MODEL OF THE ATOM

Nucleus (diameter ~10^{-15} m)

neutrons (no charge)
protons (+ve charge)

Electrons (−ve) orbit nucleus

Atom (diameter ~10^{-10} m)

Very briefly, how was the nuclear structure of the atom discovered?

Through scattering of α-particles by a thin gold foil.

The radius of an atomic nucleus is given by $r = 1.2 \times 10^{-15} \, A^{1/3}$. This implies that the density of nuclear matter is constant regardless of size. Explain how.

As A increases, nuclear mass and volume both increase in proportion ($m \propto A$, $V \propto r^3$ and $r^3 \propto A$).

X-ray diffraction is widely used to study atomic spacing in crystals. The Bragg equation, $n\lambda = s \sin \theta$, relates the spacings s of layers of atoms to the angular displacement θ of X-rays. Show that the X-rays must have a wavelength smaller than the atomic spacing.

Limiting conditions are $n = 1$, $\sin \theta = 1$. So $\lambda = s$ for the smallest resolvable s using wavelength λ.

Particle diffraction can also be used to measure atoms and nuclei. A particle's wavelength depends on its energy. Explain why electrons need very high energies to probe the nucleus.

To get short enough wavelengths ($E = hc/\lambda$).

ISOTOPES AND ELEMENTS

Fill in the table.

Symbol	Name	Description
Z	Atomic number	Number of protons
	Proton number	
A	Mass number	Total number of protons and
	Nucleon number	neutrons

Different isotopes of an element have the same number of *protons* but different numbers of *neutrons*

NUCLEAR NOTATION AND NUCLEAR REACTIONS

Any isotope of any element can be described using this notation:

nucleon number Chemical symbol $_Z^A X$
proton number

Nuclear reactions can transmute elements: true or false?   *True*
Which quantities must be conserved in nuclear reactions?   *Z, A*

Turn the page for some exam questions on this topic ►

Label the diagram opposite to show where neutrons, protons and electrons are found. Give the approximate diameters of the atom and the nucleus.

SYLLABUS CHECK
It varies from board to board how much you need to understand about other methods of probing the atom and the nucleus.

Here you need to realize that the minimum number of diffraction bands is 1 and the maximum diffraction angle is 90°.

WATCH OUT
A is mass number or atomic number; it is always an integer. Do not write 'atomic mass' (atomic mass isn't a whole number).

REVISION EXPRESS
For nuclear reactions, see the section on elements and isotopes in the Revision Express A-level Study Guide, pp. 42–43.

For more on this topic, see pages 40–43 of the *Revision Express A-level Study Guide*

EXAM QUESTION 1

Rutherford, Geiger and Marsden's study of α-particle scattering by gold foil gave the first evidence for the nuclear structure of the atom.

(a) **What was their evidence that most of an atom is empty space?**

Most α-particles passed straight through, without loss of energy or change of direction.

(b) **What was their evidence that charge and mass are concentrated in a tiny nucleus?**

Some α-particles were deflected by large angles. To get a big enough electrostatic repulsion meant the charge had to be concentrated in a tiny radius. Conservation of momentum demanded that the mass must be attached to the charge (otherwise there would be nothing to bounce off).

EXAMINER'S SECRETS
This classic experiment comes up again and again in exams. Make sure you know the set-up, the reasons for using a thin gold foil, the expected results (assuming even distribution of charge and mass) and the implications of the actual results.

Coulomb's law may give a clue to charge concentration, but why must mass also be concentrated?

EXAM QUESTION 2

The approximate radius r (in metres) of an atom's nucleus is given by $r = 1.2 \times 10^{-15} \, A^{1/3}$. **Use this equation to calculate the radius of a hydrogen nucleus ($A = 1$) and a bismuth nucleus ($A = 209$).**

$r_H = 1.2 \times 10^{-15}$ m $r_{Bi} = 7.1 \times 10^{-15}$ m

The mass of a nucleon is approximately 1.67×10^{-27} kg. **Calculate the density of nuclear matter.**

$\rho = m/V$ and $V = \frac{4}{3}\pi r^3$.

For hydrogen $V = 7.2 \times 10^{-45}$ m³ so
$\rho = (1.67 \times 10^{-27})/(7.2 \times 10^{-45}) = 2.3 \times 10^{17}$ kg m⁻³

Calculate the density for hydrogen. As an extension, you could see if bismuth gives the same answer.

EXAM QUESTION 3

(a) **Which radiation has suitable wavelengths for each application?**

Radiation	λ_{min}	λ_{max}
Ultraviolet	10^{-8}	10^{-7}
X-ray	10^{-11}	10^{-7}
Gamma ray	10^{-15}	10^{-9}

Atom separations: X-rays and γ-rays
Nuclear sizes: γ-rays

(b) **Why are γ-rays unsuitable for diffraction pattern studies?**

Random emission makes it difficult to produce a coherent beam of γ-rays.

(c) **A high-energy electron's wavelength is related to its energy by $E = hc/\lambda$. Choose a suitable wavelength to probe the nucleus then calculate the required electron energy and the voltage to accelerate an electron beam to this energy. Use these values: $h = 6.63 \times 10^{-34}$ Js, $c = 3.00 \times 10^8$ ms⁻¹, $e = 1.60 \times 10^{-19}$ C.**

Nuclear radius $\approx 10^{-15}$ m so $\lambda \approx 10^{-15}$ m
$E = (6.63 \times 10^{-34} \times 3.00 \times 10^8)/10^{-15}$ m
$= 1.99 \times 10^{-10}$ J
$V = E/q = (1.99 \times 10^{-10})/(1.60 \times 10^{-19})$
$= 1.24 \times 10^9$ V

This exam question is about diffraction techniques for measuring atom separations and nuclear sizes.

LINKS
For more information on diffraction patterns, see pp. 47–48.

DON'T FORGET
Potential difference in volts is the energy transferred to every coulomb of charge. $1 V = 1 J C^{-1}$

EXAMINER'S SECRETS
You are expected to know approximate nuclear and atomic sizes. They may not always be given in an exam question.

Nuclear energy

Nuclear energy powers the Universe!

ENERGY AND MASS

Atoms, electrons and photons are tiny. Their masses and energies need appropriate units (SI units are too big for convenience).
The atomic mass unit (symbol u) is roughly the mass of one nucleon.

1 u = one-twelfth the mass of one carbon atom

$1 u = 1.661 \times 10^{-27}$ kg
The electron-volt (eV) is a unit of energy.

1 eV = the energy used to accelerate an electron across a p.d. of 1 V ($= E_k$ gained by an electron accelerated across a p.d. of 1 V in a vacuum)

$1 eV = 1.60 \times 10^{-19}$ C $\times 1.00$ JC^{-1} $= 1.60 \times 10^{-19}$ J

1 MeV $= 1.60 \times 10^{-13}$ J

According to special relativity, mass and energy are forms of the same thing (mass–energy). It turns out that 1 u = 930 MeV.

DON'T FORGET
This is particularly useful for calculating energy released by nuclear reactions. The loss in mass tells us the energy released.

> Give the proper definition of 1 u.

> Define the electron-volt.

> Give the conversion from MeV to joules.

BINDING ENERGY

Binding energy is the amount of work required to separate all of the nucleons in a nucleus.

If it costs energy to separate nucleons, sticking them together should release energy, and up to a point that's true. But beyond iron, the costs of overcoming electrostatic repulsion between protons outweigh the energy release due to binding by the strong force.

> Define binding energy.

BINDING ENERGY PER NUCLEON

Binding energy per nucleon is a measure of an atom's stability. Any nuclear reaction that increases binding energy per nucleon will release energy.

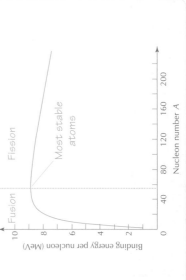

> Sketch the binding energy per nucleon.

> Mark the regions where fission and fusion can release energy.

> Mark the position of the atoms with the maximum stability.

Turn the page for some exam questions on this topic ➤

EXAM QUESTION 1

(a) Sketch a graph of binding energy per nucleon versus nucleon number. Then use it to explain why energy is released during nuclear fission of nuclei with high nucleons.

Energy release actually increases binding energy per nucleon. Fission of high A nuclei releases energy, resulting in more stable daughter nuclides.

(b) What is it called when nuclear fission occurs naturally?

Radioactive decay.

(c) Fusion of two low Z nuclei also releases energy. Why does nuclear fusion not occur naturally on Earth?

All atoms contain protons; all protons are positively charged hence mutually repulsive. Electrostatic repulsion must be overcome before the strong nuclear force can bind two nuclei together.

(d) Why is fusion possible in stars?

Because stars are hot enough. As you raise the temperature, particle speeds and energies increase. Given sufficient E_k, even repulsive nuclei will collide, allowing the strong nuclear force to act.

(e) Why must stars have a finite lifetime?

Because of the peak in the $\Delta E/A$ curve. Iron is the most stable atom. Once fusion reaches iron, no further energy release is possible.

No need to do the graph because it's the same graph you sketched on p. 67. Part (a) is just to remind you to learn it.

SYLLABUS CHECK
Some boards do not require binding energy per nucleon at AS level, but it may come up in certain options.

EXAMINER'S SECRETS
Questions like 1(c) and (d) are favourites with examiners. They test your general understanding of physics, but within a specific context.

EXAM QUESTION 2

The rest mass of a proton is	**1.007 276 u**
The rest mass of a neutron is	**1.008 665 u**
The rest mass of an electron is	**0.000 549 u**
The rest mass of a helium-4 atom is	**4.002 604 u**
The rest mass of a lithium-7 atom is	**7.016 005 u**

The mass defect of an atom or nucleus is the difference between the mass of its constituents and its actual mass. Calculate the mass defect, binding energy and binding energy per nucleon of helium-4 and lithium-7 atoms.

He $\Delta m = (4.032\,980 - 4.002\,604) = 0.030\,376$ u
Li $\Delta m = (7.058\,135 - 7.016\,005) = 0.042\,130$ u

Binding energy of ^{4}He $\Delta E = 28$ MeV
Binding energy of ^{7}Li $\Delta E = 39$ MeV
Binding energy per nucleon
^{4}He $\Delta E/A = 7.1$ MeV
^{7}Li $\Delta E/A = 5.6$ MeV

Which is the more stable nuclide?

Helium

DON'T FORGET
The differences in mass may be tiny but they are enormously important. Get used to working with highly precise data in nuclear calculations.

THE JARGON
Rest mass is the proper term for a body's mass when relativity effects can be ignored (i.e. when the body is moving far more slowly than light).

Particle physics

AQA-A AQA-B EDEXCEL

Don't be put off by the number of '-ons'; they do have a logic.

If I could remember the names of all these particles, I would have become a botanist
ENRICO FERMI

THE STANDARD MODEL

Particles can be divided into hadrons and leptons. Hadrons are made of quarks. Leptons are thought to be fundamental particles. Hadrons are subdivided into baryons and mesons. Baryons are made of three quarks and mesons are made of two quarks, or more properly, a quark and an antiquark.

Name each particle (use the symbols to help you) and give their charges.

REVISION EXPRESS
For help with this, refer to the first section on nuclear and particle physics in the Revision Express A-level Study Guide; it's on pp. 144–145.

Leptons

			Charge
e^- electron	μ^- muon	τ^- tauon	$-e$
ν_e electron neutrino	ν_μ muon neutrino	ν_τ tauon neutrino	0

Quarks

			Charge
u up	c charm	t top	$+\frac{2}{3}e$
d down	s strange	b bottom	$-\frac{1}{3}e$

DON'T FORGET
No one has ever isolated a solitary quark.

ANTIMATTER

Every particle has an antiparticle, which is identical in all respects except that it has opposite charge. The first antiparticle to be discovered was the positron (antielectron). Given sufficient energy, particle–antiparticle pairs can be created. They can also annihilate, in which case their energy is released (e.g. as gamma radiation).

DON'T FORGET
For every particle there is an antiparticle, denoted by the same symbol but with a bar over it (the bar means 'not' or 'anti').

PARTICLE RECIPES

There exist too many hadrons to remember, but you must learn the make-up of the familiar baryons, the neutron (n) and the proton (p). They are made of just u and d quarks:

$$uud = p \qquad udd = n$$

You may need to learn the make-up of pions (π^0, π^+, π^-); they consist of u and d quark–antiquark combinations. And perhaps also kaons (K^+, K^-), which are u and s quark–antiquark combinations.

DON'T FORGET
Except for the proton (p) and neutron (n), all symbols incorporate the particle's charge, giving a big clue to its composition.

Name the particles which have these quark combinations.

CONSERVATION LAWS

Name three quantities that must be conserved in any interaction.

Mass–energy
Charge
Momentum

There are several new conservation laws which are important in particle physics. Can you name three?

Baryon number
Lepton number
Strangeness

There are others but they're not needed for AS level.

Just give the basic conservation laws.

DON'T FORGET
Mass and energy are now considered as one thing, mass–energy.

Give three more quantities that must be conserved in nuclear reactions.

Turn the page for some exam questions on this topic ▶

For more on this topic, see pages 144–147 of the *Revision Express A-level Study Guide*

EXAM QUESTION 1

EXAMINER'S SECRETS
Questions asking you to work out the charge, baryon number, strangeness, etc., of exotic hadrons and mesons are fairly common. They look intimidating but they are really very simple.

Quark	Charge	Baryon number
u	$+2/3$	$1/3$
d	$-1/3$	$1/3$

(a) Give the composition, charge and baryon number for a proton and a neutron.

Neutron: ddu charge = 0   baryon number $B = 1$
Proton: uud charge = +1   baryon number $B = 1$

(b) Pions (pi mesons) also consist of u and d quarks and antiquarks. Give the composition, charge and baryon number for π^0, π^+ and π^-.

π^0: $u\bar{u}$ or $d\bar{d}$ charge = 0 $B = 0$
π^+: $u\bar{d}$ charge = +1 $B = 0$
π^-: $d\bar{u}$ charge = −1 $B = 0$
All mesons have $B = 0$.

EXAM QUESTION 2

The rest mass energy of an electron is 0.511 MeV. High-energy gamma rays may annihilate by pair production (the generation of an electron–positron pair).

(a) What is the minimum energy a gamma ray must have for pair production to be possible?

1.022 MeV

EXAMINER'S SECRETS
You will be expected to know the conversion factor 1 u = 930 MeV. You should be able to define these units.

(b) Given the mass–energy conversion 1 u = 930 MeV, roughly how much energy is required for proton–antiproton pairs to be created?

1860 MeV

EXAM QUESTION 3

Pions are up and down quark–antiquark pairs.

(a) What type of particle is a pion?

A hadron

(b) For each of these combinations, give the symbol π^+, π^- or π^0 appropriate to the particle's charge.

$u\bar{d}$
$d\bar{d}$
$\bar{u}u$
$d\bar{d}$

(c) A pion can decay into a muon. What type of particle is a muon?

A lepton

(d) What quark colour change could result in decay of a π^+ into a μ^+?

$u \rightarrow d$ or $\bar{d} \rightarrow \bar{u}$

(e) Which exchange boson would mediate this decay? Explain why.

W^+. You have to subtract a positive charge, reducing quark charge by 1 unit (e) to change quark flavour as required. W^+ has charge +1.

IF YOU HAVE TIME
Work out the quark–antiquark pairs to make K^+, K^- and K^0.

For more on this topic, see pages 144–147 of the *Revision Express A-level Study Guide*

Fundamental forces

According to particle theory, every interaction is mediated by exchange particles or gauge bosons. There is no such thing as action at a distance.

FUNDAMENTAL FORCES AND EXCHANGE PARTICLES

Every force is mediated by an exchange particle, which passes between the interacting particles. These exchanges can cause repulsion or attraction, or in the case of the weak nuclear force, changes in quark flavour plus β and ν emissions.

Force	Acts on	Exchange particle	Symbol
Gravity	particles with mass	graviton	G
Electromagnetic	particles with charge	photon	γ
Weak nuclear	all particles	intermediate vector bosons	W^+ W^- Z^0
Strong nuclear	quarks and hadrons	gluon	g

DON'T FORGET
Intermediate vector bosons are virtual particles with mass-energy so great that they can exist for only a tiny fraction of a second and are therefore confined to the nucleus.

Fill in the table to show which forces act on which particles plus the exchange particles involved.

DON'T FORGET
Gravitons and gluons are still hypothetical. Photons are particles of electromagnetic radiation. They exchange momentum between charged particles, allowing transmission of the electromagnetic force.

W^+ is released when an up (+2/3) quark changes flavour to a down (−1/3) quark, e.g. in β+ decay, where W^- decays into a β+ and a ν. W^- is released when a down (−1/3) quark changes into an up (+2/3) quark, e.g. in β− decay, where W^- decays into a β− and a ν̄. Z^0 takes part in interactions that do not produce any exchange of charge but they may still involve charged particles, e.g. e^-, e^+ pair production or annihilation.

DON'T FORGET
In the weak interaction, W^+ is involved when a positive charge is lost, W^- is involved when a negative charge is lost and Z^0 is involved if there is no change in charge.

FEYNMAN DIAGRAMS

These diagrams are a useful way of summarizing any interaction. Time runs up the page, so read from the base upwards. Particles are represented by arrows. The arrows do not show the direction of motion through space. Each vertex shows the emission or absorption of an exchange particle.

WATCH OUT
Feynman diagrams are often plotted with time running horizontally (left to right), making them look a little different. A 90° rotation will convert one type into the other.

Electron–positron attraction

Neutron decay by β− emission

Draw a Feynman diagram for each interaction.

Proton decay by electron capture

EXAMINER'S SECRETS
For any interaction, ask yourself three questions: What goes in? What comes out? What is the exchange particle? Given two of the three factors, you should be able to make an educated guess at the third.

Turn the page for some exam questions on this topic ▶

EXAM QUESTION 1

A neutron-rich radionuclide may decay by β− emission; a neutron is converted into a proton.

(a) Write an equation for this process.

$${}_0^1n \rightarrow {}_1^1p + {}_{-1}^0e^- + \bar{\nu}_e$$

(b) Which force is involved in beta decay?

weak nuclear force

(c) One type of quark has changed into another type, converting a neutron to a proton. What was the conversion?

down to up

(d) Which exchange particle is involved?

W^-

(e) Draw a Feynman diagram to represent the decay process in terms of fundamental particles (quarks, electrons and neutrinos or antineutrinos) and exchange particles.

DON'T FORGET
It was a problem with mass-energy conservation in beta decay that led to the invention, and later discovery, of the neutrino and the weak interaction.

DON'T FORGET
Neutrons are reasonably stable inside the nucleus, but outside it they decay in a matter of minutes to protons, which are very stable.

EXAMINER'S SECRETS
Check to see which Feynman diagrams are required for your syllabus, then learn them.

EXAM QUESTION 2

Name the forces that could act between these particles.

(a) Two electrons

electromagnetic, weak interaction

(b) An electron and a proton

electromagnetic, weak interaction

(c) An electron and a neutron

weak interaction

(d) A proton and a neutron

strong interaction, weak interaction

(e) A quark and an antiquark

strong interaction, weak interaction

Use the table on p. 71 to guide you; include all possible forces here.

EXAM QUESTION 3

The weak interaction is mediated by high-mass virtual particles, which can only exist for tiny fractions of a second.

(a) Why are these exchange particles virtual rather than real? Why are they not normally observed outside the nucleus?

Because their creation contravenes mass–energy conservation. They cannot 'really' exist without input of energy, but they can appear provided they disappear very shortly afterwards.

(b) Because of their large mass-energy (> 80 GeV), W and Z bosons can only exist for less than 10^{-26} second. Calculate their maximum range (if they could travel at the speed of light) and hence show why the weak interaction is normally confined to the nucleus.

Maximum range = 3.00×10^{-18} m

Smallest nuclear diameter ≈ 10^{-15} m

so W and Z bosons are normally confined.

DON'T FORGET
Heisenberg's uncertainty principle explains why virtual particles can have their short existence. For a brief instant, it seems we can violate conservation of mass–energy. Mass–energy is borrowed and paid back before anyone can detect it directly. You need to be aware of this, but you don't need to understand it.

Practical physics

Theories are revised or rejected in the light of experimental evidence. As a practical physicist, you have to be able to plan, carry out and assess experiments to test theories.

EXAMINATION AND COURSEWORK OPTIONS

Several boards offer both options. Both options assess the same skills. For most boards these skills are specified as follows.

Planning	Establishing the aim of the experiment and describing how it will be achieved
Implementing	Doing the experiment; minimizing errors by good technique; recording
Analysing	Plotting graphs; manipulating data to test predictions and theories
Evaluating	Looking at methods, results and conclusions with a critical eye

DON'T FORGET
Experiment is the basis of all science. Nothing is accepted without being tested. Every experiment really amounts to a test of a theory.

Summarize what each word means but don't go into great detail.

EXAMINER'S SECRETS
Remember to state the obvious. You'll be marked on what you write down. That's all an external examiner has to go on.

PLANNING AND IMPLEMENTING

Planning
A clearly defined aim; a prediction or theory to test; suitable apparatus and methods, with the key variable identified and other factors controlled; a suitable range of measurements planned and the need for accuracy and precision assessed.

Implementing
Safety first; accurate, systematic measurements in clear tables with units and tolerances; data and any calculated results should be to a suitable precision; systematic errors should be avoided and results repeated to reduce random errors.

Outline the essentials of your plan.

What steps will you take to get accurate and reliable results? How will you record them? What are examiners looking for?

SYLLABUS CHECK
Check what's being assessed, whether you're taking the examined option or the coursework option. If safety appears on your syllabus, then mention it in your assessed practical, and so on.

ANALYSING AND EVALUATING

Data should be manipulated if necessary to give a predicted straight line relationship which you can test graphically.

A title, suitable scales, labelled axes, units, clear points, best fit

Gradients and intercepts are often critical.

$$\text{Gradient} = \frac{\text{(increase in } y\text{-variable)}}{\text{(increase in } x\text{-variable)}}$$
Use big triangles

Give the essentials of a good graph.

How do you find the gradient?

Error bars and estimates of the possible range in a gradient can be impressive. Evaluating evidence is all about identifying errors and uncertainties. After all errors have been accounted for, if the theory doesn't fit the facts then the theory may be in trouble.

Turn the page for some exam questions on this topic ▶

EXAM QUESTION 1

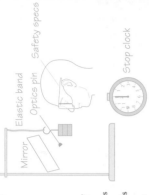

The period of oscillation for a mass suspended on a spring is given by $T = 2\pi\sqrt{(m/k)}$ where $T =$ period (s), $m =$ mass (kg) and $k =$ spring constant (N m⁻¹). This equation applies as long as the spring obeys Hooke's law. Plan an investigation to find out how the period of a mass suspended on a rubber band depends on its mass, i.e. to find out whether the equation holds for a rubber band. Do not measure the rubber band's spring constant directly.

DON'T FORGET
Good technique is essential. Mention everything you do to estimate, eliminate or minimize errors, e.g. checking micrometers for zero errors, timing oscillations from the centre where rapid motion reduces timing errors, using a fiducial mark, timing several oscillations (not just one), choosing suitably precise instruments.

Method
Safety mentioned (use safety specs). Time at least five complete oscillations for each mass. Timing starts and finishes mid oscillation (max. speed ⇒ min. timing error). Use fiducial mark at midpoint. Suitable range and number of weights (> 5).

Fill in the empty columns. Give a suitable number of significant figures. Use the data to estimate the uncertainty in the averaged period.

Results

Mass (g)	Time for five oscillations (s)				Average $T \pm 0.1$ (s)	T^2 (s²)
50	22.0	22.4	22.6		4.5	20
100	37.3	36.3	36.9		7.4	55
150	49.1	50.1	48.8		9.9	98
200	59.5	59.1	59.0		11.8	139
250	66.0	66.3	65.7		13.2	174
300	68.6	69.4	69.5		13.8	190

Graph
Plot a suitable graph to test the equation.

Within experimental uncertainties, do the results support use of the equation?

Measure the gradient of your graph, hence find the band's spring constant.

DON'T FORGET
The equation of a straight line is $y = mx + c$ where y is the y-variable on your graph, x is the x-variable, m is the gradient and c is the y-intercept.

Equation of line: $T^2 = (4\pi^2/k)m$
Gradient $= 200/0.30 = 670$ s² kg⁻¹
$k = 4\pi^2/670 = 5.9 \times 10^{-2}$ N m⁻¹

Index